MY GALLANT HUSSAR

The story of a search

Anne Batchelor

Highgate Publications (Beverley) Ltd
1993

i

This book is dedicated to George and Emma, whose story has fascinated and moved me, and to 'young George', their son, and the other Californian Batchelors without whom I would not have been able to tell this story.

British Library Cataloguing in Publication Data available

ISBN 0 948929 79 0

Published by
Highgate Publications (Beverley) Ltd.
24 Wylies Road, Beverley, HU17 7AP
Telephone (0482) 866826

Produced by
B. A. Print
4 Newbegin, Lairgate, Beverley, HU17 8EG
Telephone (0482) 886017

Cover Picture: George, my Hussar and his intrepid Emma.

Contents

Foreword

Anne Batchelor ended her previous book, *A Batchelor's Delight,* with the words 'Now how on earth can I find out who my brave young Hussar really is?' and promptly arrived in my Headquarters in York as the most enthusiastic 'sifter ' and 'delver' of records that I have ever had the pleasure to meet.

History records with great accuracy the battles and performances of regiments and their officers who aspire to positions of great leadership, but not many stories are told of young men in 'the ranks'. I was, therefore, delighted to be able to help Anne in what you will read was a monumental task.

Our regimental history books show Sergeant George Batchelor as a very distinguished soldier, but now, thanks to Anne's research, we have a veritable wealth of information within our Archives! Like a dog with a bone she will not let go and is quite ingenious in her methods of finding new tracks down which to patrol. Spanning four continents, you will thoroughly enjoy being part of 'the hunt' and the feeling of anticipation of success.

It is nice to know from our point of view that SSM George Batchelor DCM, has been given such very special treatment and that his family goes from strength to strength, albeit thousands of miles away, now having tangible proof of their distinguished relative.

CAPTAIN G. E. LOCKER
Late 13th/18th Royal Hussars
(Queen Mary's Own)
Officer Commanding Home Headquarters
The Light Dragoons (York)

Introduction

Ever since the success of my first book *A Batchelor's Delight*, I have constantly been asked, 'What about the next one?' My reply has always been, 'I do have the next book in my head already but I don't have the time to write it down — my life is so busy!' Last week I foolishly remarked to a friend that what I needed was a full week off from all my engagements and responsibilities — then I could get it written.

I now lie here in a hospital bed at Seacroft with an infected leg, under doctor's orders to stay here for an indefinite number of days to enable the wonder drugs to sort out the infection. All my classes and speaking engagements have been cancelled. This is not quite what I had in mind! However, I now have *plenty* of time, so pen in hand I recline here with a thick pad of writing paper and mounting excitement as I begin to share with you, my reader, the wonderful story of my search for my gallant Hussar.

This story begins in the same old cemetery at York where I had first discovered old Theophilus Batchelor, of whom I wrote in my first book, and it ends (if a family story can ever be said to end) in a rather grand mobile home in sunny California. It is a story of adventure, courage, humour and pathos. In these pages you will meet the sad beer-house keeper, William, who shares with me the problem of a painful leg; the intrepid Emma, a fine 'old gal'; the mysterious Tom of Hemel Hempstead; young George aged 87, who makes wonderful marmalade, and, of course, my gallant Hussar, George Batchelor.

Now read on . . .

CHAPTER ONE

The Wrong George

'I expect you have a very efficient filing system,' said the lady from the Townswomen's Guild. I gave a weak smile and said something non-committal, thinking how horrified she would be to see the chaotic heaps of files and photocopies, letters and papers which fill my flat. It is an *organised* chaos, however, and I pride myself on being able to find any document or reference within about ten minutes.

When I came to write my first book, *A Batchelor's Delight*, I had no trouble at all finding all my earliest family research notes scribbled in various notebooks over the previous six years. However, I was frustrated to discover that, as a total beginner, I had not realised the importance of copying down full details of the information I found. Thus when I wanted to tell the story of George and Eliza, my great-grandparents, I realised that all I had written in my notebook about George's death was —

> 'Cemetery Records — York City Archives —
> George Batchelor — Gas stoker — died at Layerthorpe —
> 1906'

So I wrote to the Archivist, asking for the exact wording of the entry for 'George Batchelor — who died in the year 1906'.

I received an immediate reply, with a kind offer of further help if I needed it. I looked at the burial details she had sent me and said, 'Blow me! She has sent me the wrong George!' It was my own fault, of course, for not specifying that my George was a stoker at the York Gas Works and sixty years old. How was I to know that there would be *two* George Batchelors, both buried in the same cemetery in the Spring of 1906? The man she found in the cemetery records was described as —

> 'George Batchelor — Sergeant Major in the 18th Hussars —
> Died of gangrene — buried 12th February 1906 — age 36 —
> Address — 45, Hartoft Street, Fulford, York.'

My sixty-year-old George had died of cancer, perhaps as a result of the appalling conditions in the furnaces of the Gas Works. So who was this young soldier? Had he anything to do with my York Batchelors, whose roots were in Berkhamsted, Hertfordshire? Or was his presence in the same cemetery, withing spitting distance of my George, merely a coincidence? I had that familiar feeling in my bones that he was one of us, but I had no real grounds for thinking this. How could I find out who he was? Surely with a little detective work I could identify him? 'Oh dear,' I thought. 'Here we go — Miss Marple rides again!'

I had very little to go on to begin with, merely name, regiment, age, date of death and address, so where should I begin? Having the date of death meant that I could easily obtain a copy of his death certificate. That might reveal more. A polite letter and cheque to the York Register Office in Bootham soon brought me the familiar long brown envelope containing George's certificate. This revealed two interesting details. Firstly, the cause of death given in the cemetery records was inaccurate. His death certificate said not 'gangrene' but 'hepatitus, enteritis and exhaustion.' Once again I was being reminded to treat with caution any written record, no matter how reliable it may seem to be. Only recently I collected my own father's death certificate from the Leeds Register Office, only to find when I got it home that it said, 'William Henry Batchelor — Sex — *Female.*' The cemetery records, too, contained an error. His age at death had been recorded as '74' when he was in fact 84. What confusion and frustration an error of ten years could cause some poor family historian!

Death certificate of George, my Hussar

[Printed by authority of the Registrar General.]

 CERTIFIED COPY of an
Pursuant to the Births and

 ENTRY OF DEATH
Deaths Registration Act 1953

Registration District   YORK

1906. Death in the Sub-district of York East in the York County Borough in The County of York.

No.	When and where died	Name and surname	Sex	Age	Occupation	Cause of death	Signature, description, and residence of informant	When registered
Columns.— 1	2	3	4	5	6	7	8
187	Tenth February 1906. 45 Harroft Street, York UD.	George Batchelor	Male	36 years	Quarter maater Sergeant in 8th Hussars	Hepatitis. Enteritis Exhaustion certified by Wm. Flood LRCP	Emma Batchelor Widow of deceased Present at the death 45 Harroft Street, York.	Thirteenth February 1906

Certified to be a true copy of an entry in a register in my custody.

ROBERT T. LIVESEY   RFL———.   Superintc

4. 2. 1991.

CAUTION:—It is an offence to falsify a certificate or to make or knowingly use a false certificate or a copy of a false 'certificate intending it to be accepted as genuine to the prejudice of any person, or to possess a certificate knowing it to be false without lawful authority.

2

"Scott continued to run the cemetery with a skeleton staff!"

The second interesting snippet of information revealed by the Hussar's death certificate was the existence of a widow, Emma Batchelor, '— present at the death'. Poor Emma, to lose her husband at such an early age. I wondered what I would be able to discover about her. Little did I know the amazing story I was eventually to uncover! I decided to visit George's burial plot to see whether there was a stone. Perhaps that would tell me more.

The old cemetery, on the aptly named Cemetery Road,, is a wonderful place. I love to roam its winding paths, reading inscriptions; here a tiny stone telling the poignant story of a baby who only survived a few weeks; there an impressive stone commemorating a gallant soldier. The prosperous families' stones record their success in business while the humbler folk lie under simple stones which record merely their names. My great-grandmother, Eliza, is buried there, with a stone stating, 'E. BATCHELOR'. Her George, late stoker at the Gas Works, lies in the newly created butterfly garden, old Theophilus Batchelor is under a lovely silver birch in an unmarked public grave and my own dear father rests in the shadow of the great beech tree just inside the cemetery gate.

I recently read Hugh Murray's excellent history of the York Cemetery, in which he describes, among other things, the early problems of the cemetery. One sentence caught my eye and gave me a fit of the giggles.

3

The grave of the Hussar.

'For some time,' he wrote, 'Scott continued to run the cemetery with a *skeleton* staff!' I could just see, in my mind's eye, the boney gardeners with their spades and wheelbarrows! Later he wrote, 'Another *body* appeared on the scene —' Again my wicked imagination got to work. However, in this case the 'body' was the wonderful York Cemetery Trust. Under the present Trust, supported by the Friends of York Cemetery, the whole area which was once a neglected wilderness has been transformed. Grass is mown, trees and flowers planted, the impressive chapel restored and a butterfly garden flourishes. The Victorians may have called this a 'garden of death' but it is now full of life — a riot of wild flowers and home to birds and butterflies.

On the morning I started my hunt for my Hussar's story, Bill Shaw, the Cemetery Warden, was waiting to lead me to the plot where the mysterious George was buried. I was amazed to see that there was an impressive grey stone on his plot, its inscription protected from weathering by a stone from the next row which had fallen across its face. Bill heaved the protective gravestone away and I leaned forward eagerly to read the neat lettering:

'GEORGE BATCHELOR
18 P.W.O. HUSSARS
WHO DIED AT YORK
ON THE 10th FEBRUARY 1906
ERECTED BY HIS COMRADES OF
18th P.W.O. HUSSARS
AS A TOKEN OF ESTEEM AND RESPECT

REST IN PEACE'

How very poignant, I thought, that a man whose life was spent at war should lie beneath the inscription, 'Rest in Peace'.

4

But where was Emma, his widow? I had expected to see, '— ALSO EMMA, BELOVED WIFE OF THE ABOVE,' but here was no mention of her at all. So where was she buried? I left a modest bunch of flowers on my Hussar's grave and went back home to Leeds, where I spent weeks searching the St. Cath's Index of deaths in the years following 1906. I could find no

> ## Gallant York Soldier.
>
> ### Death of Squadron Quartermaster-Sergeant Batchelor, 18th Hussars.
>
> ### HOW HE WON THE DISTINGUISHED CONDUCT MEDAL.
>
> MILITARY FUNERAL AT YORK CEMETERY TO-DAY.
>
> It is with much regret that we have to record

sign of an Emma Batchelor buried at York. Perhaps the Hussar *was* one of my Hertfordshire Batchelors and I would find his widow buried at Berkhamsted? No such luck.

I decided to turn my attention to George's birth. From his age at death I calculated his birth year as 1869 or 1870, depending on what time of year he had his birthday. In the St. Cath's Index of births there was a George Batchelor born in 1869 at Hemel Hempstead, Herts. Could this be my Hussar? I decided to seek confirmation before spending money on the certificate which might not be his.

I searched the Yorkshire newspapers for February, 1906, expecting to find a few lines in the Births, Marriages and Deaths column. There was nothing. I was so disappointed. Aimlessly I let my eyes wander across the main news columns, finding the news items fascinating. There was the sad story of two small children '— drowned in a dolly-tub' one washday when their mother's back was turned. Then there was the tale of a couple of young lads brought to court for riding on the steps of a tram! They were made to pay all that week's pocket money as a fine, less one shilling to be given to each of their mothers. That would learn 'em!

Suddenly I was stopped in my tracks by an item which filled a whole column. Sandwiched between the account of a drunken father's neglect of his children at Selby and the report of a football match between York and Selby the previous Saturday was a news item headed —

GALLANT YORK SOLDIER
DEATH OF SQUADRON QUARTERMASTER SERGEANT
BATCHELOR, 18th HUSSARS
HOW HE WON THE DISTINGUISHED CONDUCT MEDAL
MILITARY FUNERAL AT YORK CEMETERY TODAY

What a find! Here was a summary of his military career and a detailed account of his funeral. There was so much information that, in my euphoristic state, I could hardly take it in. It told me that '— he joined the 12th Lancers at an early age and after several years service in the United Kingdom he went to India and joined the 18th Hussars who were then stationed at Umballa.

On the regiment proceeding to South Africa in 1899 he fought with great distinction during the Boer War and was awarded the Distinguished Conduct Medal. He was three times mentioned in despatches by Lord Kitchener — and Lord Roberts. The Distinguished Conduct Medal was awarded to the deceased, as the regimental records bear testimony, 'for good leading in action and for covering the retirement of a wounded soldier under heavy fire' when the Hussars were engaged in a skirmish at Dulstroom, Lydenburg, on 16th April, 1901.'

The article described George as '— one of the most popular non-commissioned officers in the regiment. He always showed a good example to young soldiers, not only in the field but in garrison, by his keenness in all military duties.' That was nice, for it told me something of the character of the man. The article went on to give details of a most impressive funeral. There was a guard of honour from several regiments, which lined Hartoft Street and '— with the exception of the few details on duty at the barracks, practically the whole of the 18th (P.W.O.) Hussars regiment paraded in token of their esteem for their departed comrade.

The troops paraded in front of the deceased's house in Hartoft Street at half past ten. A firing party of the Hussars was drawn up opposite the door and, as the coffin draped with the Union Jack was carried out of the house by the bearers and deposited on the gun carriage, they presented arms and then, with rifles reversed, marched with measured tread at the head of the melancholy procession. The band . . . followed and as the cortege moved away towards the cemetery the strains of Beethoven's 'Funeral March' rose and fell in mournful cadences, and moved not a few to tears.'

What a sight it must have been. There was even a place in the procession for George's horse, led by two of his comrades, with George's boots reversed in the stirrups. On top of George's coffin were his busby-bag and his three medals. At the graveside there was a short service conducted by the minister of Priory Street Baptist Church. The newspaper report goes on, 'A hymn . . . brought the simple service to a conclusion and then the firing party came to the front. Three sharp volleys, alternating with trumpet calls, awoke the echoes, after which the troops formed up and returned to Barracks. Many people, friends of the late genial soldier, lingered behind in the warm sunshine, and bade a silent farewell to all that was left of a brave soldier and a true man.' It seemed that I had inadvertently stumbled upon a hero!

But what did the newspaper have to tell me about George's family? Not a lot, as they say! I was delighted to see that it gave his place of birth as Hemel Hempstead, a mere five miles (as the crow flies) from Berkhamsted where my great-grandfather George's family of Batchelors had lived for generations. Perhaps that feeling in my bones about the young Hussar was right — perhaps he *was* one of us. His birth date was given as 1870, but, as he was obviously in his 37th year when he died in 1906, I felt that the 1869 Hemel Hempstead birth of a George Batchelor which I had found in the St. Cath's index at Leeds had to be him. This later proved to be correct. I could now go ahead and send for his birth certificate. When that arrived it gave his parents as William Batchelor, beerhouse keeper, and Charlotte née Rickett.

Already I felt that I was beginning to put together a picture of my mysterious Hussar. The newspaper account did mention a widow though not by name — 'Quartermaster Sergeant Batchelor — leaves a widow and three children,' and later, — 'in a closed carriage rode the chief mourners, Mrs. Batchelor and Mr. Batchelor junr.' How very frustrating! None of the children were named, although the title of Mr. Batchelor junr. did suggest a lad in his late teens. This was confirmed later when I identified him as Tom, aged 17.

Armed with all this information about George, I now approached the Hussars' H.Q. in York to see what more they could tell me. First I wrote to Fulford Barracks, where he had been stationed, only a short distance from Hartoft Street where he died. They suggested that I made contact with Capt. Locker who had the regimental archives in his office in the shadow of Clifford's Tower. He was very interested in my research and told me that among their vast collection of early photographs he actually had some pictures of my Hussar's funeral. This just sounded too good to be true, so I went hot-foot to York to take a look.

As I entered the regimental office, in a state of great excitement and anticipation, I found myself at the receiving end of an ecstatic welcome — from Capt. Locker's beautiful spaniel! However, he rapidly lost interest in me when he realised that I had no biscuits or other goodies in my briefcase. There was a more subdued but warm welcome from Capt. Locker, who was to become such a valuable source of help and advice over the next year. He led me to a small, windowless room packed with files, boxes and books. From a stack of old photograph albums donated by the families of late Hussars, he produced one which contained five wonderful sepia photographs of Q.S. George Batchelor's funeral.

I could scarcely believe my luck. There were all the things I had read about in the newspaper article. There was Hartoft Street, a group of small 'street-houses', lined with the smart guard-of-honour, some bearing floral tributes. Another picture showed a group of Hussars opposite No.

The funeral procession.

The riderless horse.

45, with George's riderless horse, boots reversed in the stirrups. Then there were pictures of the military band, with its muffled drum, leading the procession across Fulford Road and into Cemetery Road. Finally there was the gun-carriage bearing the coffin, on top of which were flowers, George's busby bag and his medals. It was a very moving moment for me.

Of course, now I wanted to go and see whether Hartoft Street still existed. According to my modern street-map it was still there, so off went a letter to — 'The Occupier, 45 Hartoft Street', explaining my interest in the house and asking whether they would mind if, on my next visit to York, I called and took some photographs of the outside of the house. Back came a nice letter from an elderly lady called Ann, saying that I was very welcome to take my photographs. If I would like to let her know the date of my visit, she wrote, she would be pleased to give me a cup of tea and a conducted tour of the *inside*. This was far more than I had expected. I am always careful not to invade the privacy of the people to whom I write. I know how cautious one has to be these days about letting strangers into one's home.

On my next visit to York I turned off the busy Fulford Road and drove through the narrow backstreets, looking for Hartoft Street. Suddenly there it was — the name which had become so familiar to me as I studied the account of my Hussar's funeral, now a reality. Leaving my car at the top of the street I walked to the same spot in the middle of the road from which the funeral photograph was taken. It was a weird sensation to compare the sepia picture in my hand with what I saw before me.

Very little had changed. The skyline of the large building at the end of the street was the same. Even the street lights were in the same place, although now electricity replaced the original gas lamps. The most noticeable difference, of course, was that instead of the street being lined with soldiers, shoulder to shoulder, it was now lined with cars, bumper to bumper.

Ann was waiting at the door of No. 45 and welcomed me into her neat, spotless home. I must admit that my heart beat faster as I crossed the threshold into the very house where George and Emma had lived. Over tea and sandwiches I told Ann all I knew about my young Hussar. Then she took me on a tour of the little house. It was an exciting and strangely moving experience. I looked out through the windows at the same view of the backyard which they would have seen. 'In this room,' I thought, 'they too will have drunk tea.' It was one of those curious sensations I had experienced many times before during my family research. I had brought back the memory of them to that house and it felt as though I had just missed them — as though they had just left.

I was shown the bedroom where George must have died and the front room, the parlour, where the coffin must have rested prior to the funeral.

Hartoft Street on the day of the funeral.

Hartoft Street today.

No. 45 Hartoft Street

I remember my own mother, Frances, describing to me the sight of *her* mother's coffin in the front parlour at Featherstone. Little four-year-old Frances was really excited. 'Oh!' she said innocently. 'Have we got some new furniture?' I wondered how old Emma's children were and what they made of all the fuss that bleak February morning in 1906. I looked through the parlour window on to a street full of cars and thought of Emma's very different view on the morning of George's funeral. How she must have dreaded what had to be faced.

For me this visit to Hartoft Street marked a turning point in my research. George and Emma were no longer merely names on certificates — they were real people. I became impatient to know more about them. I wanted to trace their wedding next, but without Emma's surname that would be difficult. Once again I wrote to the Hemel Hempstead Registrar of Births, Marriages and Deaths, explaining my predicament. I said that I was aware that registrars didn't usually have time to do research, but without Emma's surname I was struck. I would be so very grateful if he/ she could possibly help me.

What a stroke of luck! My letter arrived on the desk of Faith Copley, Superintendent Registrar, and so began a friendship which has given us both such enjoyment. Instead of the usual formal letter with which I was so familiar, blankly stating — 'We do not do research — tell us the details — give us the money — we send the certificate,' I received a warm, friendly letter full of enthusiasm. Her search for the marriage of George and his Emma drew a blank, but she did come up with one goodie for me. She found the birth of a little girl, May, who was born on 2 March 1900. The parents were given as George and Emma Batchelor, formerly Redding. George was described as a Hussar, so I knew it was my family alright. So now I was looking for the marriage of George Batchelor and

11

Emma Redding. That would be simple — or so I thought.

I consulted the St. Cath's marriage index which we have on microfilm at the Leeds Reference Library. 'I should find it in an hour or so,' I thought, 'then I'll go and do some shopping.' Silly me! I was still there at closing time, getting increasingly frustrated. I looked for them marrying between 1885 (when George would have been sixteen) and 1906 (when he died). After all, he could have been under age when he married, like my great-grandfather who was seventeen but gave his age as twenty-two. George the Hussar just was not there. There was no George Batchelor anywhere in the country who married an Emma Redding or Reading. I was so frustrated.

I visited the Library again and again, grasping at straws and looking for George Batchelor/Bachlor/Batchellar/Bakeller, who married *any* Redding/Reading girl. There was nothing. As a wise man once said, 'This way madness lies!' I wondered whether he was known as something other than George? After all, my uncle Curly was born Robert but was Curly to everyone all his life. I well remember how strange it seemed at his funeral when the vicar spoke about '— the familiar sight of Robert on his bike, coming home from his allotment.' We all wondered who Robert was!

Similarly, outside the Middlesbrough Crematorium chapel where my Auntie Dolly's funeral was to be held was a noticeboard giving her name as *Annie* Batchelor. When I remarked on this to my mother she said, 'Oh yes, I knew she was really Annie. Do you know how she came to be called Dolly? She was born at home, you see, and when the midwife brought her downstairs to show to the other children, her young brother said, 'Oh, she's just like a little dolly!' So the name stuck.'

Imagine if you were trying to find *her* on the St. Cath's Index. You would expect to find her under 'D' for Dolly, or perhaps Dorothy or Dolores, when all the time she would be hiding in the 'A' section as Annie. No wonder family historians tear out their hair when their ancestor appears to have never been born or buried! I wonder how many Joshuas are masquerading as Sam, or Gertrudes as Daisy?

So painstakingly I looked for *any* Batchelor marrying *any* Redding *anywhere* in the country between 1885 and 1906. I spent hours and hours, weeks and weeks, with no sign of them. I would stagger out of the St. Cath's room, boggle-eyed after another fruitless afternoon, muttering under my breath, 'All right — I know when I'm beat, but you wait — next time —!'

At that time the 1891 Census had not yet been released from its cloak of secrecy, so there was no help for me there. Instead I asked Faith at the Hemel Hempstead Register Office for Emma's birth certificate. She proved to have been born in the same town as George, so why weren't they married there — or anywhere else for that matter?

I was getting nowhere at all with this line of enquiry. When confronted with this sort of brick wall (familiar to all family historians) I find the wisest move is to leave it alone and go and do something else. I decided to turn my attention to George's army career and try to forget the elusive wedding. There were surely lots of official records I could study? Capt. Locker of the Hussars came up with some brief references to my George in a printed history of the regiment, including details of the action which earned him the D.C.M:

> 'Sergeant Batchelor, with six men of 'B' Squadron, were following up the Boers into the rocky country which lies to the west of Kranspoort, and had advanced some distance from the main body of 'B', who were leading the advance, when about forty of the enemy, having collected together, made a furious attack on him; he had good cover, however, handy, and taking every advantage of it, he held his own in the rocks, knocking over several Boers as they incautiously dashed on what they thought was their certain prey.'

George was also mentioned in the *London Gazette* on March 25th, 1901.

> 'Sergeant Batchelor, 18th Hussars, for repeated good service, and especially at Franzpoort, near Middleburg, on 8th December, 1900.'

He was mentioned in Army Orders, too —

> '18th Hussars
> 3854 Sergt. G. Batchelor.
> At Dullstroom on 16th April, 1901, Boers all round his front and flanks and firing heavily, lay amongst some rocks and kept them off whilst a wounded man retired to safety.'

I fairly glowed with pride as I read about my Hussar. What a man! The regimental history gave details of the engagements in India as well as South Africa. I was able to plot George's movements from place to place across both continents. I was amazed at the distances travelled by this cavalry regiment —

> 'May to July, 1901 — total mileage — 570 miles
> September to November, 1901 — total mileage — 668 miles
>
> November, 1901, to February, 1902 — total mileage — 1,108 miles'

In one of his letters to me Capt.. Locker wrote, 'Cavalry was certainly cavalry in those days, and the bond that must have developed between man and horse must have been richly rewarding to those concerned.' I'm

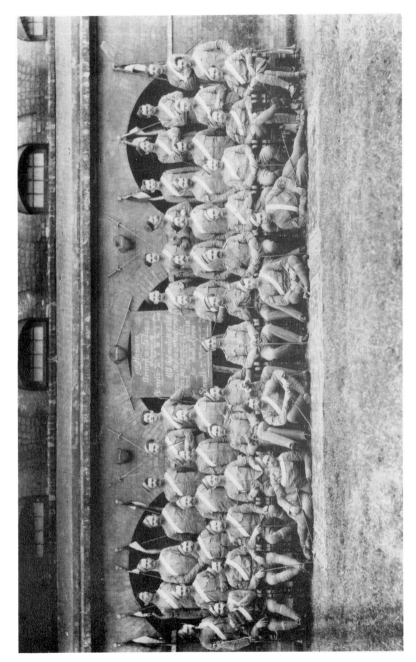

All that remained of my Hussar's regiment after their years in India. George is there somewhere, but I can't identify him!

14

glad that George's horse went with him on his last journey up Cemetery Road.

Now I began to wonder where George's medals were. It was likely that his family still had them, wherever they were, but there was just a possibility that they were in some military museum. I employed my 'pebbles in the pool' technique, tossing numerous letters into the postbox every day. This kind of saturation bombing usually works, one letter eventually bringing back an exciting response. This time, however, I had no joy. Disappointingly neither the Imperial War Museum, Sotherby's, the Hussars' Museum at Cannon Hall nor any other recipient of my letters could come up with news of George's medals. They appeared to have sunk without trace. Another dead end.

I decided to turn my attention in yet another direction. It was time I worked out whether there was indeed any relationship between my Hemel Hempstead Hussar and my Hertfordshire ancestors. After all, that was the original question which began my search. Using information from the St. Cath's Index, the amazing I.G.I. (Mormon Index), Census returns, parish registers and wills from the Buckinghamshire and Hertfordshire Record Offices, it was possible to put together a family tree for my Hussar. I was delighted to discover that George's family could be

Anne and Mary researching in the Record Office.

15

traced back to a Benjamin Batchelor of Hawridge, Bucks., who married Elizabeth Atkins at Chesham in 1746. There were Batchelors in Hawridge prior to that date, according to the Bishop's Transcripts. A Daniel Batchelor described as '— a rich man,' was buried there in 1719, while Benjamin (a youth) was buried in 1705 and Joseph (a yeoman, not rich) in 1702. Now *my* Batchelors were in Hawridge in 1636. It proved difficult to research the years between George's ancestor, Benjamin, in 1746 and my ancestor, John, who died there in 1636, for the Hawridge records are not complete. It is quite probable that the two families are related, but I may never know for sure. Hawridge is still a very small community and for two unrelated Batchelor families to have lived there in the 17th and 18th centuries is highly unlikely. All the Batchelors in the Bucks/Herts border villages seem to be descended from the same Hawridge/Aston Clinton/Chesham stock.

So far, so good. What next? Could I perhaps pick up someone in York who knows the descendants of the Hussar's family? I wrote an article about my research and my anxiety to trace any surviving members of his family, and sent it to the local press with a request that they publish it. It sank into a 'black hole' and I heard nothing more of it. I shrugged my shoulders and tried another tack. I wrote to Priory Road Baptist Chapel in York, because their Rev. J. Morrison Cumming had conducted the Hussar's funeral. They sent me a kind letter and a history of their church, but they could find no reference to George Batchelor or his family.

I re-read the newspaper account of the funeral, looking for clues. I noticed that the Fulford District Conservative Club had sent a floral tribute. I was getting so desperate for a lead I would try anything, so I sent them a letter. This caused a flurry of interest among their members, but no one knew the family. In their reply, however, they did tell me that they had found Serg. George Batchelor's name on their list of members for 1906 but nothing more. George and Emma's three children seemed to have vanished leaving no descendants. Curiouser and curiouser!

Then came my moment of inspiration which was to dramatically change the course of my search and eventually lead me to my goal. I came across a copy of the article I had written for the local newspaper and decided to send it to the *Hemel Hempstead Gazette*. It was just possible that someone in George's home town might be able to help me. I wrote a covering letter to the Editor, explaining what I was trying to do. After a pause came a reply from someone called Nicholas Jones, with a copy of the article which had appeared that week. He wished me luck and asked me to keep him informed of my progress, with a view to doing a follow-up a few months later.

Time passed. A few weeks went by. Then one evening I had a telephone call which left me grinning like the Cheshire Cat. The conversation went something like this —

'Hello — is that Anne Batchelor?'

'Yes —'

'My name is Ann Sugars and I'm ringing from Southampton.'

'Yes?' (I began to wonder whether she was selling double glazing!)

'Well, a friend of mine in Hemel Hempstead cut out your article and sent it to me because my name was Ann Batchelor before I was married.'

'What a coincidence.'

'It's even more of a coincidence than that — you see, your Hussar was my grandfather's brother!'

I was thrilled to bits. Here at last was someone who knew of my Hussar. She would be able to answer all my questions — or so I thought. I told Ann all I knew about George and Emma, and asked what she could tell me about the descendants of their children. I felt quite deflated when she told me that she knew nothing at all. All she did know was that her grandfather, Joseph, was born in Hemel Hempstead, the son of William and Charlotte, née Rickett, and that he had a brother, George, who was in the Hussars.

I sent Ann a copy of my Hussar's family tree, which matched the tree which she and her husband had drawn up for her family. I also sent her

Fulford Barracks, York, where George was stationed in 1906.

copies of wills of some Hawridge Batchelors, who were her ancestors, and promised to keep her informed about any further progress.

It was very satisfying to have found Ann, but so frustrating, too. After all my research, all my demented 'Miss Marple'-ing, I was no nearer to finding out my Hussar's full story. I knew so little — he had married Emma Redding at some unknown place at a date I could not discover. They had three children, one of whom was May, one male child who was a teenager in 1906 and one other child of unknown age and sex.

As so often happens in family research, the trail came to a dead end — or so it seemed. I was extremely disappointed to have done so much work for so little result. How was I to know what exciting discoveries were in store for me — just around the corner?

A Hussar officer with his busby bag

CHAPTER TWO
'A bit queer in the head!'

I continued to keep in touch with Ann Sugars in Southampton, sending her details of her Hawridge ancestors as I came across them. Then one day she asked me for some specific help. Apparently her father used to tell her that his grandfather, William Batchelor of Hemel Hempstead, fell in a canal when drunk, and drowned. She thought that it happened around 1900. 'How can I find out if that was true?' she asked. William would have been my Hussar's father. What an irresistible challenge! I couldn't wait to start.

I sat down to think it out. That is the aspect of family history research that I love — the mental gymnastics; the guessing and 'perhaps-'ing; the sifting of clues; the use of the imagination and reasoning. I call it, 'Playing Miss Marple'. The first obvious move was to find William's death certificate. I wrote to my good friend, Faith, at the Hemel Hempstead register Office. Could she find the death registration for me? I took Faith's letter to the post-box that same afternoon — and had a very alarming experience.

I put my hand on top of the box as I popped my letter in, and thought to myself, 'That's warm. The sun must have heated it up.' My letter fell to the bottom of the post-box with a gentle thud and a puff of *smoke* shot out of its mouth. This was followed by an alarming gush of smoke which curled up around the lid. It really was very spectacular — like Indian smoke-signals!

Being quick witted I acted at once. I rushed at an old gentleman in a nearby garden who was quietly hosepiping his lawn. At first I'm sure he thought I was a mad woman when I asked him whether his hosepipe would reach the post-box. Of course, it was too short, so he ran inside and returned with a full watering-can. It must have been a lovely sight — these two worried looking people emptying a watering-can into the mouth of a smoking post-box! People walked by and stared, but being

The exploding post-box.

very English no one wished to appear nosey enough to ask what on earth we were doing.

I contacted the Post Office, who sent someone to take a look at the dripping post-box. They assured me that there was no real damage done, due to our prompt action with the watering-can. The contents of the box, including my letter to Faith, were all slightly charred and soggy, but none had been destroyed. If the ancestors were up to their usual tricks of putting the 'mockers' on my research, it would take more than an exploding post-box to stop me now.

Faith received my request for details of William Batchelor's watery end. She came up trumps with a certificate full of information. It told me of William Batchelor, 69-year-old beerhouse-keeper and carter, of London Road, Boxmoor, Hemel Hempstead, who died on 10 September, 1900. Place of death was given as 'Grand Junction Canal' and cause of death as 'Drowning — but whether such drowning was accidental or otherwise there is not sufficient evidence to show.' How fascinating! Did he fall — or was he pushed?

The death certificate also mentioned a coroner's inquest. That might be worth following up. However, that proved to be little help to me, for I discovered that coroners are not obliged to keep their records for very

CERTIFIED COPY of an   ENTRY OF DEATH
Pursuant to the Births and   Deaths Registration Act 1953

Registration District   HEMEL HEMPSTEAD

1900   Death in the Sub-district of   Hemel Hempstead   in the   County of Hertford

Columns	1	2	3	4	5	6	7	8
No.	When and where died	Name and surname	Sex	Age	Occupation	Cause of death	Signature, description, and residence of informant	When registered
155	Tenth September 1900 Grand Junction Canal Boxmoor U.D.	William Batchelor	Male	69 years	Innkeeper and Carter	Drowning but whether such drowning was accidental or otherwise there is not sufficient evidence to show	Certificate received from Lovel Smeathman Deputy Coroner for Hertfordshire Inquest held 10th September 1900	Eleventh September 1900

Certified to be a true copy of an entry in a register in my custody.

K.U.Smeathman   Deputy   Superinten

18 September 199

Death Certificate of William Batchelor

long, neither do they deposit them at Record Offices. They are officially destroyed after quite a short period, genealogically speaking. So I sat and pondered on my next move. Had I been a cartoon character, a little light bulb would have appeared above my head at this point. THINKS! Of course — my friend Nicholas Jones at the *Hemel Hempstead Gazette* had said,' If ever there is any help I can give you —.' Surely the unexplained death by drowning of a local innkeeper might have some mention in the newspaper.

I gave him a ring and explained the story, with the exact date of the inquest which had been given on the death certificate. He was so intrigued that he dashed off right away to search for poor old William. In only a matter of days I held in my hand a photocopy of the *Gazette's* coverage of the incident. It was just wonderful! The article, dated Saturday, 15 September, 1900, carried the headline —

'OLD MAN'S SUICIDE AT BOXMOOR'
and below that —
'GOT UP AT MIDNIGHT TO DROWN HIMSELF'

That was very misleading, for at the end of the article it clearly stated that the inquest jury returned an open verdict *and* the death certificate noted that there was not sufficient evidence to show how he came to drown.

Nevertheless it was an amazingly detailed article of over six hundred words. After listing the members of the jury it first explained briefly the known facts of the case —

'It appears that the deceased, William Batchelor, was an old man and lived alone with his wife at the beerhouse where the inquiry took place.

HOUSES			NAME and Surname of each Person	RELATION to Head of Family	CON-DITION	AGE		Rank, Profession, or OCCUPATION	
In-habited	Unin-habited (U.), or Building (B.)					Males	Females		
1			Fanny Slade	Wife	Mar		49	Sal. Paper Mill	Herts
			William Batchelor	Head	Mar	59		Lab.r	Herts
			Charlotte D.o	Wife	Mar		32		Herts
			William D.o	Son	Unm	11		Scolar	Bucks
			Joseph D.o	Son		10		D.o	Bucks
			Henry D.o	Son		4			Herts
1			George D.o	Son		1			Herts
			Thomas Brice	Head	Wdr	72			Herts
1			Mary D.o	Daur	Unm		50	Dressmaker	Herts
			James Cook	Head	Mar	36		Lab.r Paper Mill	Herts
			Ann D.o	Wife	Mar		26		Herts

My Hussar as a baby, living with William (later keeper of the Three Crowns, Boxmoor).

Some weeks ago he hurt his leg in the act of moving some wood and the wound never properly healed. This seemed to prey on his already weakened mind and at midnight or in the early hours of Monday morning he got up from his bed and told his wife that he was going to the back yard. However, he did not return in a reasonable time and his wife called a son who lives a few doors off. After making a search for several hours, the body of the old man was found in Pepper's Lock, but as to how he got in the water there is no evidence to show.'

The reporter then went on to assume — 'With no financial or other troubles attendant it can only be supposed that the deceased committed suicide by drowning himself whilst in a state of temporary insanity.' The jury, however, came to a different conclusion after hearing all the evidence. I too had my own theory about how William met his end in Pepper's Lock, but more of that later. The first person to give evidence was Charlotte Batchelor, wife of the deceased *and* mother of my Hussar. To quote the *Gazette* —

'She said her husband was 69 years of age. He was a carter and beerhouse keeper. His legs were generally weak, and lately he had been queer in the head. Owing to a bad leg he had been unable to work for some weeks and this made him very downhearted. On Sunday he was a little more cheerful than usual. He went to bed at 10 o'clock. About five minutes to one he woke witness up by getting out of bed. She asked him where he was going, and he said he was going to the back. She listened for him but he did not return, and a quarter of an hour later she got up and called him, but found he was not where he said he was going.

She then called her son, a few doors down the road, and he went to look for deceased. She knew nothing further until her son returned and said the body had been found, and a little later deceased was brought home. He had no money troubles whatever.'

Next evidence was given by William's son, Henry, the brother of my

Hussar. Henry said that he had noticed that his father had been distressed of late. He told how —

'That Monday morning his mother called him up, and said deceased had gone out somewhere. He got up and after searching for a time in vain called P.C. Turner and later P.C. Boarder. They each went a different way and searched all over Boxmoor and Apsley. It was arranged that they should meet at Apsley, but as the constables did not turn up witness made his way back up the towing path of the canal.

When he got to the High Bridge he saw three or four men, and a man named Wallis told him that a body had been pulled out of the canal. When he got to Pepper's Lock he saw P.C. Turner standing by the side of the body. Deceased was then conveyed home in a cart.'

Next one of the policemen gave account of that frantic early morning search for the missing William —

'P.C. Turner deposed that he in company with P.C. Boarder and the last witness made a search for deceased. When near Pepper's Lock witness saw a cap floating on the water in the lock. He got the winch and lowered the water, and was then able to see the body. With help he got the deceased out of the water and found the body quite dead and stiff. Upon searching witness found 13s, and a knife. He then went for medical assistance. It was just 5 o'clock when the body was found.'

Finally evidence was given by Dr. Erskine who told how —

'He was called to the "Three Crowns" and on going found the body of deceased in an outhouse. Upon examination he could find no external marks of violence. Death was caused by drowning.'

The jury, after a brief deliberation, returned an open verdict, *not* one

Birth Certificate of my Hussar,
showing him as son of William and Charlotte, later of the Three Crowns.

[Printed by authority of the Registrar General.]

	CERTIFIED COPY of an		ENTRY OF BIRTH					
	Pursuant to the Births and		Deaths Registration Act 1953					
Registration District			HEMEL HEMPSTEAD					
1869 .	Birth in the Sub-district of		Hemel Hempstead		in the	County of Hertford		
Columns	1	2	3	4	5	6	7	8	9
No.	When and where born	Name if any	Sex	Name and surname of father	Name, surname, and maiden surname of mother	Occupation of father	Signature, description, and residence of informant	When registered	Signature of registrar
340	Fourteenth April 1869 Two Waters	George	Boy	William Batchelor	Charlotte Batchelor formerly Rickett	Farm Laborer	X the mark of William Batchelor Father Two Waters Hemel Hempstead	Twenty Fifth May 1869	William Frowd Registrar.

Certified to be a true copy of an entry in a register in my custody.

CAUTION:—It is an offence to falsify a certificate or to make or knowingly use a false certificate or a copy of a false certificate intending it to be accepted as genuine to the prejudice of any person, or to possess a certificate knowing it to be false without lawful authority.

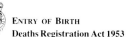

Deputy *Super*

12 March 1991

of suicide as claimed in the *Gazette's* somewhat sensational headline. There was rather a touching gesture from the jury, at the end of the inquest, when the foreman — 'kindly handed over to the widow the fee allowed the jury, it being understood that she was not left in the best of circumstances'.

Poor old William — what a way to go! Yet as I said before, I have my own ideas about what happened that cold September morning. As I write this from my hospital bed, with my sore leg hot and throbbing, I have a great fellow-feeling for the old lad. If his wounded leg, too, was infected it would have become very hot in bed, as mine is. When he got up to visit the loo down the yard, he probably decided to go for a walk in the fresh night air to cool it down. Finding himself on the towpath, the cold water of the canal would have seemed very enticing — not for ending his life but simply as a leg-coolant! I know that a stretch of icy-cold water would have been a great attraction to *me* and my leg this week!

Perhaps the poor old fellow simply sat down on the canal side to dip his leg in the water. He could easily have lost his balance and fallen in. After all, he would be sleepy and not completely *compos mentis*. According to an ex-nurse friend of mine, his leg injury which would not heal up, and the descriptions of him by Charlotte as 'queer in the head' and by his son, Henry, as 'distressed,' suggest that he was suffering from septicaemia (blood poisoning) which could have affected his mind and clouded his judgement. It could even have caused him to faint and fall to his death in the icy water.

Of course now I had an irresistible urge to visit Pepper's Lock — if I could locate it. I was given the address of a canal museum at Stoke, but they could not help. However, they kindly passed me on to British Waterways who came up trumps. They sent me a photocopy from their old records showing a William Pepper living in the lock-keeper's house at Lock 64. There, without question, was my Pepper's Lock. They also sent me detailed maps of the canal to help

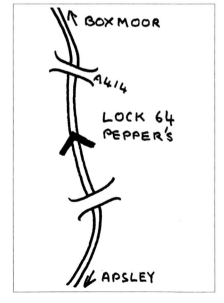

Map of canal.

me find the very spot. Later the 1891 census showed William Pepper living there with his widowed mother. There was even a footpath leading from London Road, where William had the 'Three Crowns' beerhouse, to the side of the lock-keeper's house. I couldn't wait to travel south and stand at the very place where poor William died.

So one Autumn morning I rose at the unearthly hour of 4 a.m. to catch the 6 a.m. Rapide coach south, with the familiar tingle of excitement and anticipation which marks all my family history expeditions. Would I really find Pepper's Lock? Was there still a 'Three Crowns' at Boxmoor? I took my camera with me to record the historic visit and off I went. Because Faith Copley, the Hemel Hempstead Registrar, had been in on my research of the Hussar and his family from the start, she was eager to join me in my hunt for Pepper's Lock. Also joining me would be my good friend, Mary Geary, whose search for her late mother's Batchelor ancestors led to our meeting about seven years ago, since when she and her husband, Ernie, have opened their house to me whenever I need somewhere to lay my weary head when researching in Bucks. or Herts. One day we shall, at long last, sort out the 'William and Hannah' problem which has plagued us for years, and shall know for certain how we are related, as we indubitably are.

The three of us headed first for the area of Boxmoor where William had his beerhouse (and where my Hussar would have lived in his younger days).

I doubted whether the 'Three Crowns' would have survived, though I had an excellent description of it from a bill of sale —

> '— being of brick and small part flint-built and slated and containing entrance lobby, taproom, bar, wash-house, three bedrooms and two attics. The out-premises comprise brick-built and tiled warehouse with loft over, long timber and slated stable, offices and enclosed yard. Water is laid on. The frontage is about 28ft.'

Quite an impressive building for a mere beerhouse! The lot was sold to a Mr. Cox for £570.

We found an excellent pub, the 'Princes Arms', for our bar lunch before going to look for Pepper's Lock. Pubs are a much neglected source of local information for the visiting family historian. I have never seen them mentioned in any 'How to do it' book on family history, but I heartily recommend a visit if you are in a strange area and want some family information. The locals at the pub and the cleaners/flower ladies at the church often know more about local families than the vicar, who may be a recent in-comer.

At the 'Princes Arms' we got into conversation with 'mine host' and a couple of customers. The publican told us that his pub had originally

The Princes Arms.

The towpath to Pepper's Lock, Boxmoor.

been a beerhouse with its own brewing facilities in the back, one of many on the London Road opened to serve the hundreds of navvies employed to excavate the canal.

We explained about William Batchelor and the 'Three Crowns', and our quest for Pepper's Lock. One of the customers told us where we could find what he believed to be Pepper's Lock. It was the only Boxmoor lock with the remains of a house, he told us, and it was close to the 'High Bridge' mentioned in the newspaper account of William's death. So, map in hand, we set off. It was an eerie sensation to walk along the towpath from the High Bridge towards the Lock, knowing that we were following in the very footsteps of young Henry Batchelor as he searched frantically for his missing father in the early hours of that dark September morning.

We reached Lock 64, and there, sure enough, was all that remained of William Pepper's house. It was overgrown with weeds and there were very few stones left, but from the wrought-iron fence it was easy to make out the dimensions of the house. Beside it was a stile and a footpath leading across a field in the direction of London Road and the 'Three Crowns.' Was this indeed the very spot where poor William came with his throbbing leg and confused mind? It was a moving moment for me as I looked into the deep, dark water, whipped up by a strong Autumn wind.

We took lots of photographs of the lock, the towpath and bridge, and then stood together discussing old William's fate. At that moment we saw a figure approaching along the towpath. It was an old man, walking with a pronounced limp! As he drew level with the three of us, he scowled thunderously at us as if to say, 'What do you think you are doing here? Clear off!' He then turned towards the lock and started to walk the narrow path across the top of the lock gate. As he dragged his lame leg along, his foot caught several times on the uneven surface. For one awful moment I thought he was going to lose his balance and fall in. The three of us watched his slow progress with bated breath.

Perhaps *this* is how old William fell in. Another explanation was taking shape in my mind. The story in the *Gazette* mentioned his cap floating on the water in Pepper's Lock. Perhaps it was blown off his head into the water and he went up on the gate to try to retrieve it. It would be easy in the dark to stumble and fall, especially in William's condition. I had the foolish fancy that this man might have come along to show us how it happened. I was so mesmerised, watching his slow and tortuous progress to the safety of the far bank, that I never thought to take his photograph. It would have been interesting to see whether his figure would show up, on top of the lock gate. Perhaps not!

Readers of my first book, 'A Batchelor's Delight', will no doubt remember the weird problems I have had with mysteriously blank rolls of film from a camera in perfect working order, and cameras which fail to function at all. It is perhaps significant that the only photograph taken of me on my own camera at Pepper's Lock was a complete blank! All the other photographs taken there were fine. Were the deceased Batchelors up to their usual tricks — or was it after all only coincidence? Luckily Mary managed to get a photograph for me on her camera, as a souvenir of my visit to Pepper's Lock.

We rounded off our day with a search for the site of the 'Three Crowns.' The 1871 census had shown it to be just beyond the gasworks on London Road. Alas, the area had been cleared and there were now new homes built on the site. A quick trip further down the road brought us to Apsley End, the birthplace of my Hussar's bride, Emma Redding. The census showed that her parents had a draper's shop. Now it is the local newsagent's run by a charming Asian lady.

It was with a deep sense of satisfaction that I left Boxmoor that afternoon, I had made my pilgrimage to Pepper's Lock at last. I had solved the mystery of Ann Sugars' family story, gathered a little more information about my Hussar's family *and* restored the good name of old William Batchelor the beerhouse-keeper. He had not been drunk, after all — just a bit 'queer in the head'!

At Pepper's Lock.

CHAPTER THREE

'I am George!'

That's the trouble with family history — it is so easy to be led astray from the mainstream of your research by some fascinating story such as that of the beerhouse-keeper of Boxmoor. I had put aside my work on my Hussar because I seemed to have reached a dead end. Now I felt that I ought to have another go.

In my experience, when confronted by the dreaded 'brick wall' which defies all efforts to break through, it is often a good idea to approach the problem from another angle — to go *round* the wall if you can't get through it. I call this, 'thinking sideways'. Apparently its real name is 'lateral thinking.' Sounds very grand!

To give an example, when seeking information on the Bloggs family of Yorkshire, if there are no Bloggs wills or other family documents, it is always worthwhile looking for documents of families who married Bloggs men. Thus you may find William Bloggs' father-in-law, Farmer Midden, leaving something in his will '— to my loving daughter Mary Midden, now the wife of William Bloggs of Folly Farm, Garforth.' Now you have the name of William's farm, which could lead you on to other sources.

So, to try to sidestep my dead-end brick wall, I decided to approach George and Emma from another angle. For a long time I sat and chewed over what I already knew. I went back and re-read all my information. I kept coming back to the thought that *Emma* was the key to the next part of the story. There she was, a young widow with small children. How would she feed them and pay the rent? There was no Family Credit or Income Support in 1906. So she must have had other income. She might have gone to work — but where? More likely she would have taken in work, for the children would have been too young to leave. To find these details would probably be impossible.

Then came a flash of inspiration. Of course! Why had I not realised it

Umballa (Ambala).

before? As the widow of a serving soldier she would surely have received a Widow's Pension! My book on the records held at the Public Record Office told me that such records were at Kew. Because of the problem of getting out as far as Kew on a day visit to London, I decided to use the services of a search agent.

I had met June Underwood through our mutual membership of the Buckinghamshire Family History Society and knew of her excellent work as a researcher of Army records at Kew. I wrote her a long letter, telling her all I knew of George Batchelor's military career, and asked her to search for some record of Emma's Widow's Pension. There was the usual nail-biting pause, during which I kept telling myself that I had probably sent her on an expensive wild-goose chase. Then one wonderful morning my postie brought me a huge brown envelope with June's name on the back. It was so thick and heavy — she *must* have found something.

With trembling fingers I tore it open and pulled out the contents. There were eight large folded pages of photocopied material on bright yellow paper. The very first page took my breath away and I had to sit down at once to compose myself. Then I tried to read my goodies quietly and calmly:

'I, Emma Louisa Batchelor, do solemnly and sincerely declare that I was lawfully married at Umballa, India, on the 30th day of March, 1896, to No. 3854 Squadron Quarter Master Sergeant George Batchelor, 18th Hussars, who died at

45, Hartoft Street, York, on the 10th day of February, 1906, aged 36 years.'

Well blow me! *India!* No wonder I could find no record of their marriage on the St. Cath's Index. I read on —

'— the following are the names and dates of birth of the late S.Q.M.S. George Batchelor's legitimate children now living;
William 1st November 1897
May 2nd March 1900
George 9th September 1906'

All their children at one fell swoop! I could hardly contain my excitement.

Another page gave more details of their Indian wedding. The witnesses were Albert and Alice Tuley, and the marriage was performed at the Methodist Church by Rev. Enoch Jeffreys. This page also gave the place of birth for each child — William at Lucknow, India; May at Hemel Hempstead when Emma returned to England in 1900, because George's regiment had been sent to South Africa to fight in the Boer War; finally young George, born in York seven months after his father's funeral. All three were described as 'not baptised'. Reading those details through, it did strike me as strange that at the funeral in 1906 Emma was described as having *three* children. As she was only two months pregnant with young George, they would hardly have counted him, would they? Curious, I thought.

All the documents made fascinating reading. There were some medical details —

'There is no record of this soldier having any illnesses in South Africa, but the Medical Officer states that his death was caused, doubtlessly, by his war service in South Africa, and thinks that such service may have been a predisposing cause to the contraction of the disease.

A.M.D.2.

Do you consider that this man's death was due to illness contracted or commencing on *active service* in South Africa?'

A.M.D.2.

Yes, we consider death should be attributed to War Service.'

The same letter also notes that poor George had dysentery while in South Africa, being admitted to No. 12 Field Hospital 28.12.1900; transferred to No. 17 Stationary Hospital 4.1.1901; and discharged to duty 22.1.1901. Such a wealth of detail.

There was even one document asking Emma for a copy of her birth certificate on which she had written her reply —

> 'In 1906 I had to get a birth certificate for the Royal Patriotic Fund as I received a pension from that fund for a year or so before I got an Army pension. I suppose they still have it, but I think I have given the correct year of my birth.   E.B.'

It was so moving to read those words in Emma's own hand.

The really mind-blowing discovery was contained in two documents relating to Emma's later pension payments. One gave her change of address in 1918 and the other the address at which she died on May 6th 1953. Both addresses were in — California, U.S.A.! No wonder I had trouble finding descendants in York. No wonder there was no mention of a loving widow on George's tombstone. What a turn up for the book!

But how on earth could I hope to find Emma's family in America? California is an awfully big place. It would cost a fortune to employ a researcher. After all, I had so little to go on. In 1918 Emma was at 419E, Maitland St., Ontario, California, and she died at Pomana, California, of cerebral vascular thrombosis, thirty-five years later. Was this now the end of my story? Had I reached my final dead end?

I decided to share all these final discoveries with Ann Sugars in Southampton. After all, the Hussar was her grandfather's brother. I rang her and told her the amazing news of the Indian wedding and Californian death. 'Goodness me,' said Ann, 'I have an old aunt in her nineties who used to write to someone in California *years* ago. I wonder whether she still has the address?' I could hardly believe my ears. Was it possible that I might find some of my Hussar's missing family after all?

I doubted whether Auntie would even remember writing the letters back in the 1960s, let alone still have the address, but hope springs eternal — and you just never know in this game. Bless her cotton socks, old Auntie *did* still have the address, which she gave to Ann. She wrote at once, to the address in Vista, California, explaining our interest in the family and asking whether the people there knew anything of George and Emma.

Back came a reply, via Ann in Southampton. It was a most wonderful letter which, I must confess, almost moved me to tears. It declared —

> 'I am George, the last of their children.'

I felt as though I had won the pools! Here was young George, the little boy born seven months after his father's death, named after the brave Hussar and now 85 years old. Who would have believed it possible to find him after all these years?

George's wonderful letter also contained something I had longed to see — a photograph of his parents with one of their children. At last I was

> *8 18 91*
>
> Dear Ann –
>
> I have put together all the information that I have, regards to George Batchelor & their family. I am George, the last of their children.
>
> I have inclosed several pictures

My first letter from George.

able to look on the faces of my George and Emma. What a strange sensation, after all these months of searching, to be able to look them in the eye. I must admit that in the case of George, having read of all his courageous military exploits, I was expecting a Charleton Heston or perhaps even Rambo! Instead I got — Hercule Poirot! He was slight of build, a dapper man with a waxed moustache and dark hair brushed flat. Still, he was my Hussar at last. What a thrill!

Emma was just as I had imagined her — calm and composed, a capable-looking woman, bonny rather than pretty. I wondered how she came to be in India. Had it anything to do with her parents' drapers shop? Could she have gone to India to buy exotic materials such as silk? It hardly seemed likely for a small village draper at Apsley End. Later, in the India Office records, I found a trade directory which listed an H. Batchelder (the common Hertfordshire spelling of our name) who was an assistant at Whiteway Laidlaw & Co., general drapers in Calcutta. The directory mentioned that they were importers of stores and had a branch at Lucknow — where my Hussar's son, William, was born. Mere coincidence, perhaps, but the Hussar had a brother called Henry.

On that exciting morning when I received my first letter from my Hussar's last surviving child, breakfast was forgotten as I sat down at once to introduce myself to young George aged 85, pouring out on paper all I knew about George and Emma. How wonderful at last to be able to share the results of my research with their family.

While I awaited young George's response to my great bundle of information, I decided to have a flying visit to London to find documentation on the wedding in Umballa, India. Another 4 a.m. start (I must be mad!) and I arrived, bleary-eyed and half asleep, at the India Office Records in Blackfriars. After the usual fiasco of '— the microfilm of the record you wish to see appears to be missing —' (which I come to expect when the ancestors seem to be putting stumbling blocks in my way) I had a nail-biting, clock-watching *two hour* wait while the very helpful staff tried to trace the inexplicably missing microfilm. Time was running out and my return coach left Victoria at 6 p.m. At last I reaped my reward. Because of my sheer persistence in not giving up but sitting tight, thereby being an embarrassment to the long-suffering staff, they brought me a huge, crumbling file of *original* marriage licences. What a bonus! The public are not usually allowed access to the actual documents, so, instead of thwarting my research, this problem of the missing film meant that I was able to see George and Emma's actual signatures written on their wedding day. Another thrilling experience for me.

Emma's signature was small and precise, as I would have expected. George's was in a large, bold hand which reminded me of the signature of my 8xgreat-grandfather, William Batchelor, parish clerk of Rickmansworth. Their ages were given as '26 $^{11}/_{12}$' for George and '27 $^{6}/_{12}$' for Emma. They looked more like hat sizes than ages! Again let me warn my reader, even official documents such as marriage licences cannot be trusted. Emma was, in fact, 29 $^{11}/_{12}$. Of course, I could actually have found their marriage on the *special* St. Cath's Index of Marriages Abroad, had it occurred to me that theirs was an overseas marriage. As it was, I stumbled upon it by happy accident through Emma's pension record. Serendipity rules, O.K.?

As usual when doing my research, I couldn't resist being side-tracked by some interesting material at the Record Office. In the trade directory for Calcutta I found a reference to a school in Shambazar Street. The assistant teachers were — A. P. Chuckerbutty, M. L. Chuckerbutty and G. C. Chuckerbutty. The Head Pundit was Bissumbhur Chuckerbutty

Signatures from the marriage certificate.

and the assistant Pundit Saweswar Chuckerbutty. What a lovely name. I wonder what the collective noun for such a group would be? Perhaps 'a chatter of Chuckerbutties' if they were very talkative, or 'a chortle of Chuckerbutties' if they laughed a great deal? Or perhaps bearing in mind its Indian location, 'a chitty of Chuckerbutties'? Anyway, I think it's a lovely name and it certainly made me smile. I also found one of those useless pieces of information I can't resist — between Happy Valley Tea Estate and Sunny Sight, the Rajah of Cooch Behar had a place called 'Bachelor's Cot.' Not a lot of people know that! But I'm rambling again. Back to my Hussar.

At last I received the long awaited letter from young George. I continue to call him this to avoid confusion with his father, George the Hussar. Over the next months our letters hurtled back and forth between Yorkshire and California, bringing us both such pleasure and excitement. I sent him masses of photographs, including one of the house in Frances Street, York, where he himself had been born. I told him that he should be very proud to be a genuine Yorkie!

I sent him his father's funeral photographs, which he had never seen, the house at Apsley End, Hemel Hempstead, where his mother was born, pictures taken at Pepper's Lock (plus the newspaper account of his grandfather's watery end), a map of South Africa showing his father's travels during the Boer War and other material relating to his father's military career.

I was even able to send him photocopies from the Hemel Hempstead school log book which mentioned his big brother, Bill. —

'MAR 10 1903 — Admitted Wm. Batchelor, aged 7, a very backward boy from Whelpley Hill School, near Chesham.

NOV 17 1905 Removed W. Batchelor's name from the register.'

Poor Bill was certainly not backward. He was probably still suffering culture shock, having spent the early years of his life in the very different surroundings of India. This last entry was very important to me, for it helped me pinpoint the date the family moved to York. William left his school in November, 1905, and his father, my Hussar, appears on the membership list of the Fulford Conservative Club that December. So it seems that George and Emma had been in York less than three months when he died.

Young George sent me some more wonderful photographs, including one of himself as an appealing little six-year-old at school in Hemel Hempstead (— or possibly York?) and one labelled, 'The day we left England for U.S.A. — 1913,' which showed an elderly-looking Emma, aged only 47, with Bill, May and young George, aged six. He sent me a

Young George at school.

"The day we left for USA" —l to r — Young George (aged 6), Bill, Emma and May.

Emma with her grown-up family — l to r — Young George, May, Bill and Tom, with a couple of grandchildren.

sent me a later photograph of the same group taken when Emma was an old lady, which included someone called Tom, whom I took to be a relative or family friend. More about him later!

There was a photograph of what George called a piece of cloth, which proved to be the insignia from his father's uniform, which he would have worn on his sleeve above his sergeant's stripes. It was touching to think that Emma removed it from his uniform after his death and had treasured it, taking it all the way to America with her. Her son also has a badge from his father's uniform which indicates that he was a small arms instructor. When I first started my hunt for my Hussar I had no idea that I would be able to learn so much about him.

Young George sent me photographs of his impressive mobile home, surrounded by orange trees and beautiful rose bushes and flower beds. He told me that his father's name lived on in his family, and sent a photograph of himself, George; his son, Richard George; his grandson, Donald George and his great-grandson, Michael George. That pleased me very much. It was a nice tribute to the father that young George had never met. There was a grand photograph of Emma in her seventies, too,

Insignia about 4½ in x 3½ in.
Red background – gold lacement.

Insignia about 2½ in x 2 in.
Red backing – gold lacement.

showing the same determined face she had shown to the camera in 1897. George described her, with great pride, as 'a fine old gal!'

I asked George about his father's medals, but he had no idea what had become of them. I pestered him about his early memories of England and the long journey to California. There was so much I wanted to know. His memory for detail was wonderful. He wrote —

'We boarded a French ship that left from Southampton. It was a very rough trip. I remember every sea-sick day of it. Along with my daily sickness I can still hear brother Bill groaning and calling, 'Please throw me overboard!' Guess we all thought better to drown than this.

Emma in her seventies
("a fine old gal").

38

'We finally landed at Philadelphia not New York as intended. We had to board another hateful boat and went on to New York. We had to spend three days in the Immigration Building, Ellis Island, which we soon renamed the 'monkey house' — iron bars on all the windows with us as the monkeys. We could look out of the windows and see the Statue of Liberty — sure never impressed any of us very much!

Aunt and Uncle finally found us and we went on to New Jersey. We were fourteen days after leaving England before arriving at New Jersey. Today it would take only a few hours. Boy, how things change! Later we went by train all across America — over 5,000 miles and several more days. How Mum ever got us all there, I often wonder.'

Poor little George, what an ordeal it must have been. How he must have yearned for the security of the life he knew in England. What a remarkable woman Emma must have been. Not only had she travelled halfway across India to find her Hussar, but now she crossed the Atlantic with her fatherless children and set off across the American continent to make a new life for them in California. I take off my hat to you, Emma! How I wish I could have met you.

George's letter went on —

'Later in life I was back in New York on business and I climbed to the

Young George with his wife Carrie.

39

top of the Statue of Liberty. Looking out of the window, I could see our old 'monkey house'. It looked as grim as ever. I read now where they are going to restore it to its original state. If they were to ask me, I would say, "Blow the darn thing up!"'

George told me about his growing-up years in California and how he married his school sweetheart, Carrie, sixty-three years ago. He told me what had happened to Bill and his sister, May. Then, calamity! He threw a massive spanner into the works of my carefully researched story. I had asked him why the family had gone to America. His answer left me puzzled and confused. He said —

'Tom went first. He was unable to find employment he liked in England so he decided to try America. His Aunt May (Emma's sister) lived there. He arrived at Aunt May's in New Jersey, but not liking that, he went on to California where May's husband had a brother in the lumber and building supply business. I guess it was then he had the idea of building a house and having Mum bring the rest of us over.'

All very interesting — but who one earth was Tom? George said that he was at my Hussar's bedside when he died, so he must have been a close member of the family — but why had I not come across him before? I read on. That was when young George delivered his bombshell.

'My sister, May, married Charles, who was working for *brother* Tom.' Brother Tom? Who on earth was he? According to Emma's pension records from Kew she only had three children — William, May and young George. I took out all my notes on the Hussar's family and read them very carefully.

According to Emma's declaration in 1906, William was the first legitimate child of George and Emma, being born in India a year after the wedding. No mention of a son called Tom. I asked George for more information, saying that his reference to Tom had puzzled me. He wrote back that Tom was born in 1889. I saw at once that this was seven years before the wedding. Curiouser and curiouser!

I decided to call in the help of my good friend, Faith, at the Hemel Hempstead Register Office. She could find no 'Thomas Batchelor' in the register of births for 1889. Then I had one of those blinding moments of sheer inspiration. 'Was there a Thomas *Redding*?' I asked. After all, the pension record did specifically use the word 'legitimate' when listing George and Emma's children. Could there have been a child before the wedding? Faith came back to the phone, her voice breathless with excitement. 'Yes, indeed! There *is* a Thomas Philip Redding born in 1889. His mother is given as Emma Louisa Redding, domestic servant, and the father's column is blank.'

What a turn up for the book! So Emma had Tom seven years before her marriage to my Hussar. That, of course, threw up two important questions — was George the father, and if he was, why did they wait so long before

George's luxurious mobile home in California

marrying? As so often happens in family research, the answer came from an unexpected quarter.

I was on holiday in Scarborough and got into conversation with a lady at my hotel. She told me that her grandparents were married at Gretna Green. When I asked the reason she said, 'Because he was a serving soldier, and Army regulations forbade marriage before the age of twenty-six.' How old was my Hussar when Emma married him? *Twenty-six*! So it would appear that they had to wait until 1896, whereupon Emma caught the first boat to the Far East and travelled hundreds of miles across India to find and marry her Hussar. What a determined lady!

Now, of course, I had another problem. Do I tell young George? People of his generation are often embarrassed by such skeletons in the family cupboard. The last thing I wanted to do was to upset him. At first I tried to skirt round the truth about Tom but he was so insistent that I should discover the truth about Tom's identity that in the end I had to explain the circumstances of Tom's birth. I need not have worried. Young George was most understanding. He wrote, 'I don't think any less of Mum and Dad or Tom because of the facts. Events of this nature have happened many times in the past and will happen many times in the future.' I was so relieved.

Letters and bundles of photographs continued to fly back and forth between us, gradually filling in the blanks in my Hussar's biographical jigsaw puzzle. Most movingly of all, George shared with me many things which his dear mother had told him of her early life. She remembered living at the draper's shop at Apsley End and being got out of bed by a neighbour who urgently needed to buy 'A paper of pins'. She spoke often of her life in India. George wrote —

'I remember Mother telling about their life in India. It must have been a very enjoyable time for them. She would tell about having several "boys" working for them, one for housekeeping, one to go to the market for their daily needs, then to come back and cook their meals. Their cottage was one large open room with bamboo separators that hung from the ceiling making several small rooms. These separators were called 'punkahs'. Each had a string tied to them and that string went over to a boy's toe. He sat in a corner and kept his foot moving, thus keeping the punkah swinging and the air circulating. With all that, who needs electric fans? She also mentioned that Dad had his own polo pony, so I guess they did quite well.'

With all this lovely information, I was still greedy for more. I asked George how his mother managed to bring up her children with no husband to support her. He did not seem to mind my insatiable curiousity, but sent me more and more details of their life. He wrote —

'At no time did I ever feel we were hard-up. We never had maids or butlers, but neither did any of our neighbours so that was no problem. I'm sure Tom and Bill contributed. I know when I started working at odd jobs, I did. We always had a garden with lots of fruit and vegetables. We had chickens, rabbits, fresh eggs, etc. We usually had a beef roast with Yorkshire Pudding on Sunday, and every now and then a beef steak pudding. Of course at Christmas time there was always plum-pudding, made in enamel pots that Mother brought from England. Incidentally, we still have one and Carrie uses it for the same purpose.'

I love getting letters from George. They are so full of information and written with such warmth and humour. I had to smile when he wrote, at the end of one letter which covered six sides of foolscap, 'I really don't talk this much but it seems when I start writing there is no place to stop!' I know the feeling. My letters usually begin, 'Dear George, This is just a quickie —' and then go on for seven or eight pages.

He ended one of his letters with a comment on getting old — 'Someone asked an 85-year-old fellow how he felt to be that age. His reply was that he never felt his age, in fact he never felt anything until about noon and by then it was time for his nap!' Again, I know the feeling. It was common knowledge at the school where I used to teach that Miss Batchelor got there at 8.30 a.m., but she never woke up until 11. They used to swear that I drove there on automatic pilot!

A lovely surprise came as a result of getting in touch with Winnifred, the widow of the Hussar's son, Bill. I wrote her a long letter, telling her

The Medals

of my interest in the family and mentioning that I would be most grateful for any help she could give me. Her reply had me whooping with delight. She wrote that 'Emma and I were good friends and spent many hours together and she told me of her years in India. My son, James, *has three of his grandfather's medals.*' How wonderful! In a later letter came some excellent photographs, showing the precious medals I had striven so hard to locate. How very satisfying to have found them at last. I was so glad that they were still in the family and not in the hands of a collector.

Yet more photographs arrived from young George — lovely, domestic treasures brought to America by Emma and passed on to her children. There was a pair of china lions which had sat in the fireplace of the Redding's home in Apsley End, and a Coronation mug bearing the picture of the King and Queen and the inscription 'Apsley and Nash Mills'. There were Emma's silver opera-glasses and a glass candy dish in the shape of a train. Most moving of all, there was a simple shoe-horn used by my Hussar to help him put on his shoes. Wouldn't he be surprised at the delight such simple, everyday objects gave me?

One morning I had a surprise visit from a postman bearing a large oblong box. It had, on the outside, a picture of a Pyrex-type coffee pot. 'Are you sure it's for me? 'I asked, 'I haven't ordered anything from a catalogue.' 'Well, it has your name on it,' said the postie. 'It's from America.' Puzzled at why my American Batchelors would be sending me a coffee pot, I opened it carefully. There, nestling in masses of thick padding, were two jars of homemade marmalade, bearing the label, 'George's Special.' It was, too. Absolutely delicious!

One thing saddened me about my contact with my Hussar's last surviving child. I don't suppose I shall ever meet young George in person, for now 87 years old he would not be able to travel all the way across the Atlantic to visit his birthplace in England. Family responsibilities here make a visit to California out of the question for me. I therefore decided that if we couldn't meet, we could at least talk in person. I sat down with my telephone directory and planned a telephone call to California. I crossed my fingers that the ancestors would refrain from tinkering with our 'phones!

I chose a Sunday in June for our historic conversation. Very carefully I worked out the best time of day to ring. A mistake in my calculations and I could be getting poor George out of bed in the middle of the night. Heaven forbid!

I warned him, by airletter, what I was planning to do. I didn't want a repeat of the fiasco last year, when I rang my Australian penfriend to wish her a happy Christmas. On that occasion I thought I had planned everything carefully, even making notes of what I wanted to say to Bev,

The four generations of Georges — Michael G, Donald G, Richard G and 'Young George'.

to make full use of the time I would have with her. I did all my sums and had everything worked out down to the last detail — or so I thought. With great care I dialled her extremely long number. A mistake here and I might find myself talking to someone in Liechtenstein or Botswana! I heard the 'phone ring in Bev's Sydney home and then — oh horror, the voice of an answering machine! Bev and her husband were away on holiday!

That taught me a lesson. Nothing like that was going to spoil my first live conversation with my Hussar's son. With mounting excitement I watched the clock creep round to 8 p.m. on the evening of Sunday, 6 June. It seemed to take *forever*. At one point I even wondered whether the clock had stopped, and double-checked with both my watch and the kitchen clock. At exactly 8 p.m., with trembling fingers, I dialled young George's fourteen figure number.

After only a moment I heard the long note of his 'phone as it rang so many thousands of miles away in sunny California. A male voice answered. 'May I speak to George Batchelor?' I asked. Back came the wonderful response 'This *is* George.' It was a magical moment. Haltingly at first, we began to talk. It was such a strange sensation. This man was a total stranger I had never met — yet I knew him so well. As we spoke I had a mental image of that little six-year old, his arms folded, sitting to attention on an old kitchen chair having his photograph taken on the day he left England in 1913.

Gradually we relaxed and began to speak as we write — jumping from one subject to another, joking and laughing, eagerly plying each other with questions. As one who talks with her hands, I was aware of gesticulating wildly, though I knew full well that he could not see me.

It was so lovely to hear George say repeatedly, 'I remember —.' I would have thought that all his years in America would have dulled his memories of his early years, but that was not so. He remembered fish and chips wrapped in newspaper; succulent pork-pies from the local shop; wagons rumbling along the cobbled road outside his home in Hemel Hempstead; milk being delivered by cart and measured out in a tin jug, and, most thrilling for me, he spoke of his memories of his remarkable mother, Emma.

We talked at some length about her and her amazing journeys, first to India to marry her Hussar and then right across the American continent to California. 'She was a most determined woman,' said George, 'When she made up her mind to do something, she did it.' That was just what I felt she would be like, this young woman who gazed calmly at me from her photographs. I can imagine the horror in her parents' home when she declared, 'I'm going to India!' Of course, there would be no stopping her.

Young George and I continued our happy conversation, both of us agreeing that George and Emma would have been so pleased to know that we were in touch at last. I was introduced to Carrie, young George's childhood sweetheart who has been his wife for sixty-three years. In return I introduced them to my mother, Frances, who was thrilled to be sharing this special moment with me. I told George that as soon as this book about his parents was finished he would be given the very first copy — autographed, of course.

Then, sadly, it was time to say our farewells. I promised to ring again another day, and our wonderful trans-Atlantic conversation was over. I could hardly believe that it had gone without a hitch. What a marvellous invention the telephone is! Afterwards I sat down to think over all that was said and began to glow with satisfaction. How lovely it is that my research has brought me so many new friends and given such happiness to me and to them.

When I look now at the amount of material I have gathered over the past couple of years, I really am amazed. I started my search knowing so little about my Hussar — merely a bald statement in a cemetery register. Now the gallant George and his intrepid Emma are real people to me. It has been so satisfying to share their story with their son and to know that, in far away California, they will be remembered with pride by later generations of their family. I feel sure that my George and Emma would be pleased about that, too.

Postscript

With a lump in my throat I stood in the front parlour of 45 Hartoft Street, and gazed out on a silent street lined with cars. Through the same window, eighty-six years ago, poor Emma had seen the crowds gathering to pay tribute to her heroic young husband. The guard of honour were already in place. She would have heard the subdued chatter of the neighbours, the impatient snorting of horses and the jingle of harness. Perhaps the military band had already struck up its first sombre notes. No doubt Emma hugged her young children to her before stepping out to face the ordeal of public mourning, following her young hero husband on his last short journey to the cemetery. How I felt for her, sensing her grief across a gulf of almost ninety years.

It seems to me that this is what family research is all about — reconstructing the past but also reaching out to individual men and women as we recognise our common humanity. The detective work involved in tracing the story of George and Emma has been fascinating and great fun, but to live through their lives with them has been a great privilege.

FAMILY TREE OF GEORGE BATCHELOR, 18th HUSSARS

Benjamin Batchelor of Hawridge — married at Chesham in 1746 — Elizabeth Atkins

Benjamin Batchelor — married at Hawridge in 1781 — Mary Taylor

Benjamin Batchelor x 1788 Hawridge — married at Chesham in 1809 — Sarah Barnes

William Batchelor x 1811 Hawridge — married at Hawridge — Maria Thorn

Children: Anna x 1816 Haw., James x 1818 Haw., Kitty x 1821 Haw.

William Batchelor born c. 1832 (Beerhouse-keeper) — married at Chesham Dec. 25 1858 — Charlotte Rickett of Waterside.

Children: William x 1859 died in infancy?, George Latimer x 1860 Chesham, William x 1860 Chesham, Joseph x 1861 Chesham, Henry x 1867 Hemel H.

George Batchelor the Hussar x 1869 Hemel Hempstead died at York 1906 — married in 1896 Umbala India — Emma Louisa Redding x 1866 Apsley End, Hemel Hempstead died in California 1953

Children:
- Thomas P. Redding born Hemel Hempstead 1889
- William married Winnifred Born Lucknow India 1897
- May married Charles Born Hemel H. 1900
- 'Young George' married Carrie born 1906 in York
  - Richard George
  - Donald George
  - Michael George

x = Christened
c = circa
Haw. = Hawridge, Bucks.
Hemel = Hemel Hempstead, Herts.

Acknowledgements

Family history research depends for its success on the help and co-operation of many people, both in their official capacity and as private individuals.

I must record here my gratitude to Capt. G. Locker of the 18th (Q.M.O) Hussars, (now the Light Dragoons), for the interest and enthusiasm he has shown and for his extreme patience in answering my many questions over the past few years. I am indebted to him for granting permission for the use of material from the Regiment's archives.

My thanks are due also to my wonderful Superintendent Registrar at Hemel Hempstead, Faith Copley, for helping me find details of my Hussar's family and for sharing with me my expedition to Pepper's Lock.

I owe a tremendous debt of gratitude to Ann Sugars of Southampton, for without her help I would never have found 'Young George' and the rest of my Californian Batchelors.

I am grateful to Nicholas Jones of the *Hemel Hempstead Gazette* for the great interest he has shown and the invaluable help he has given, and I here express my thanks to the *Gazette* for allowing me to use material from their past issues.

My thanks to Hugh Murray for allowing me to quote from his excellent book, *This Garden of Death*, and to my good friend Ron Sudderdean for the use of his cartoons.

My thanks to the Warden of the old York Cemetery, Bill Shaw, for his help in locating my Hussar's grave and for the tremendous work done by Bill and his team in converting the cemetery from a garden of death to a place of life and beauty.

The signatures from George and Emma's marriage certificate are reproduced by permission of the British Library.

I must here acknowledge permission granted to me by the Office of Population Censuses and Surveys for the use of various certificates, the design of which is Crown Copyright and which are reproduced with the permission of the Controller of Her Majesty's Stationery Office.

49

Acknowledgement is due to the Controller of H.M.S.O. for the use of Census extract (Ref. RG 10/1387 fol 59) which is Crown Copyright.

My gratitude to Janice Brooker and the staff of the Hertfordshire Local Studies Library for their ongoing interest in my research and their practical help, and to the extremely helpful staff at my local library at Seacroft.

The photograph of Umballa, now known as Ambala, is used by kind permission of the Archivist at the British in India Museum at Colne, Lancashire.

I am deeply indebted to Ann Coman of Hartoft Street, York, for welcoming me into her home where my Hussar lived with his Emma.

My grateful thanks to George, Winnifred and James Batchelor of California, U.S.A., for lending me their precious original family photographs and for sharing with me their memories, without which this story would have been incomplete.

My dear friends Mary and Ernie Geary provided me with accommodation in their lovely home in Ampthill whenever I researched my Hussar's Hertfordshire roots, and kept me going with endless 'tea and sympathy' as I struggled with genealogical brick-walls. My thanks to them both.

Finally I must record my gratitude to Irene, Martyn and John of Highgate Publications, Beverley, for their continued encouragement, and for producing such a lovely book. They have made an old man in California very happy!

Benjamín Prado was born in Madrid in 1961. He has published several volumes of poetry and a series of novels: *Raro* (1995), *Dónde crees que vas y quién te crees que eres* (1996), *Nunca le des la mano a un pistolero zurdo/Never Shake Hands with a Left-handed Gunman* (1996) and *Alguien se acerca* (1998). *No sólo el fuego/Not Only Fire* was first published in Spain in 1999, and won the prestigious Premio Andalucía de Novela.

BENJAMÍN PRADO
Not Only Fire

Translated by Sam Richard

faber and faber

First published in Spain as *No sólo el fuego* in 1999
by Alfaguara
Torrelaguna, 60. 28043 Madrid

This translation first published in the United Kingdom in 2002
by Faber and Faber Limited
3 Queen Square London WC1N 3AU
This paperback edition published in 2003

Typeset by Faber and Faber Limited
Printed in England by Bookmarque Ltd.

This publication has been translated with aid from the General
Department for Books, Archives and Libraries of the Spanish Ministry
of Education, Culture and Sports.

A CIP record for this book is available from the British Library

ISBN 0–571–20901–7

2 4 6 8 10 9 7 5 3 1

Not enough, no, not enough
the sunlight nor its warm breath.
The uncertain mystery of a glance – not enough.
The rustling fire in the woods one day – hardly enough.
I learned about the sea. Even that is not enough.

Vicente Aleixandre

CHAPTER ONE

I

'They say that you can't die in a dream; that if you ever saw death staring you in the face – a woman pointing a gun, a wolf in mid-leap, a man brandishing a knife or rope or hammer – your heart would stop.' Truman paused, slowly allowing the words to fill the room, to form and become almost solid beings whose presence, on resuming the story, would remain there, all around them, in the red of the chairs, or dissolved in the sweet taste of the drinks left by the door like a gravedigger's boots. '... Perhaps you won't know what I mean, but you can't be alive on this side and dead on the other.'

In later life, in different settings and situations, they would recall, never quite knowing why, that they had been talking about this shortly before it all started, as again and again they went over to the windows to watch a venomous sky extend its menace over the darkened streets of the city centre, where people ran for shelter under the downpour, basements flooded, and fire-engines forced their way past drivers listening on the radio to news about the comet.

A couple of kilometres away, the children's father gazed out at the storm from inside a bus, while in another room of the apartment, standing motionless by the balcony, his wife rehearsed the words she would use that evening to say she was going to leave him.

The man on the bus was called Samuel and the woman by the balcony was called Ruth. On leaving his office, half an hour earlier, Samuel had followed an unknown girl in the street. He followed her without knowing why; he saw her buy a magazine, stop to look in several shop windows, make a call from a public telephone. As she began to glance at him over her shoulder – once, twice, three times, first with an arrogant stare, then a cautious gaze, finally an anguished look – her strides grew less assured, more hesitant, as if she were walking over the wet flagstones of a sloping pavement; until, suddenly, she turned a corner and broke into a run. He halted his pursuit and stood for a moment watching her flee, feeling a cold dark wind on his skin, a wind strong enough to tip over empty chairs and fling the flowers off graves.

At six o'clock, when she entered the living room where Truman was talking to Marta and Maceo, Ruth had the distinct impression that what was about to take place between herself and Samuel made her surroundings seem strange: the drinks cabinet, the carpet, a red armchair, the telephone, a leaded window – each item seemed to conceal a menace, a secret, to be part of an opening scene in the kind of story that might feature an abandoned house and a small white coffin, a dead woman and a pistol that lay buried at the bottom of a river.

She looked out again at the street: the horizon had turned dark to the east; flashes of lightning cast sudden murky light over the rooftops; claps of thunder sent cowering dogs into kitchens littered with broken glass. As the regular thud of a meat cleaver rose from the butcher's below, she reminded herself that this was another reason to leave – that horrible noise which, day after day and hour after hour, filled her head with images of animals severed in half, of knives clutched in white, bloodstained hands.

While Truman continued telling some story or other to the children, Ruth observed the manner in which Marta was listening: the look of indifference or boredom on her face as she cupped her chin in her palm, the way her mind appeared to be elsewhere, always just beyond the reach of her grandfather's voice. Ruth thought Marta fairly beautiful – she was slender and she had an attractive face, though it was perhaps the kind of beauty which needed to be given a chance and which, without a second glance, ran the risk of passing unnoticed. Ruth pictured her growing up, abandoning her studies, marrying the least talented son of a rich family. On the morning of the wedding, several years later, Ruth and Samuel would meet again as they took their places together at the front of the church, and he would say to her: 'I wish I had never let you go.'

Then came the death of Marta's husband, the vast inheritance, the long trip mother and daughter made through Europe: she could still recall afternoons spent cruising on high seas, the leisurely approach of the trains into Moscow or Athens. One night, as they dined in a small restaurant in the port of Ankara or perhaps a hotel in Berlin, Ruth heard the sound of Samuel closing the door to their apartment, twenty years earlier.

'*Un*believable – garages flooded, trees down, traffic in complete chaos, phone lines on the blink . . . The entire city is at a standstill! And wherever you go, you're bombarded by all the bank and shop and car alarms set off by the thunder.'

Samuel paused in the doorway to catch his breath and Ruth shuddered at the sight of his wet shoes, pale raincoat, and those devastating swamp-green eyes, which, in some way, formed an integral part of his reputation, of the image he gave of being a decent and sincere person.

'Several fires have broken out in the old city and lightning shattered one of the statues in the Retiro Park. I heard that passers-by collected the pieces and took them home,' Samuel went on, plugging in the television, perhaps to find a weather report or any news that would confirm what he was saying: images of flooded streets, of damaged buildings, of lorries abandoned in the downpour.

'In the park?' said Truman. 'Which statue?' But Samuel ignored him, and carried on:

'It was so dark by five o'clock that the street lamps came on. Shortly afterwards, the system collapsed. Apparently the power cut left most of the trains stranded. Imagine what an absolute mess that caused – all those people cooped up in carriages like animals, for over two hours, in the middle of open fields or stuck outside stations, trapped in tunnels . . .'

'Did the police do it?' Maceo asked.

'Do what?'

'The street lamps. Did the police turn them on?'

Samuel gave him a furious look. The boy's strange ideas, and the absurd way he always interrupted conversations at the oddest moments, so annoyed Samuel that he often felt a kind of blind fury, a violent impulse so hard to control that once, during the Christmas holidays, in the middle of a square full of acacias decorated with white bulbs, he had given Maceo a resounding slap. And now, all of a sudden, memories of that afternoon flashed through his mind in a succession of small details – the dry fountain, a yellow overcoat, the snow dirtied by numerous footprints – from which he accurately and unhesitatingly pieced together the whole episode, like a man who imagines an entire war on seeing seven or eight old bullet-holes in the wall of a cemetery. Maceo, too, remembered the episode, which would remain with him in the months and years to come. On an August morning, many years later, while walking in the woods with his wife or as he lay down beside her on a beach, he would suddenly hear the sound of the dry leaves crunching underfoot or notice the disagreeable sensation of the wet sand against his skin, and say: 'Did I ever tell you about the time my father slapped me on Christmas Day, by a fountain in the middle of a square?'

'The street lamps are activated automatically,' Ruth interrupted.

Samuel switched channels, glanced back at Maceo and almost at once – in a manner so incongruous as to make him wonder whether other people also possessed this insoluble mix of conflicting emotions – his anger gave way to a surge of unbridled love: this boy means so much to me, he's so sweet, so innocent, I'll do everything I can for him, teach him whatever he wants to know.

'That's right,' he said, 'they're equipped with sensors to measure levels of daylight. When the daylight drops below normal, the street lamps come on automatically.'

On screen, a female newsreader was describing a tropical storm and the ferry that had sunk off the coast of Manila; survivors were swimming in a ten-kilometre oil slick, in shark-infested waters. Maceo wondered if it was true what Truman had once told him, that sharks slept with their eyes open.

'I don't believe it! Madrid is about to collapse and these people are talking about the Philippines!'

As she watched him unplug the television and explain to Marta and Maceo how any increase in voltage caused by the current atmospheric conditions could damage the electrical appliances; as she watched him leave the room sadly, or wearily, shaking his head as though to say: 'If that's the way things are going, what's this country coming to?' – and then slowly walk down the corridor, pausing on his way to the bedroom to switch off lights that had been left on; Ruth found she no longer had an explanation for whatever misfortune or wrong decisions had led Samuel to become the man she now saw. She closed her eyes and saw herself on an October morning, twenty years earlier, dressed in a peach-coloured skirt and jacket, in a lecture hall of the Faculty of Arts. She could almost revert to being that girl, who in 1977 had never been one for speeches or strikes or meetings, and who on that particular day had been afraid that a group of fascists armed with knives, chains, or baseball bats would barge in at any moment, as she stood there listening to some students pass on what seemed to her muddled orders, in words that were both too grand and too empty. She leant against the wall and searched her handbag for cigarettes, glancing to her left and right as if about to cross a street. 'Five more minutes,' she told herself. 'Then I'm out of here.'

From the dais in front of the blackboard the speakers had to raise their voices to make themselves heard above the confusion, as they delivered emphatic, defiant statements with a passion she found ridiculous. She sat down and took out a pen and pad; she began by drawing a vague shape; then attempted a self-portrait, trying to capture – though without success – the slightly feline eyes, the straight line of the nose, the cheekbones that lent her features a certain severity. Suddenly she realised the room had fallen silent, looked up, and saw Samuel.

Even now, so many years later, when on the point of leaving him for ever and with something inside her associating that separation with the blows that resounded from the butcher's – with the sliced-open carcasses lying on slabs – Ruth needed only to close her eyes in order to relive every one of the sensations she had felt that morning, to become once more that girl seeing Samuel as he slowly walked to the platform and stared back at his audience.

'I wonder what all of you are thinking?' he began, and Ruth stopped her self-portrait, suddenly captivated by the sight of the young man in the red shirt, who glowed amid the gathering as if wrapped in flames. 'I wonder if you think that making a lot of noise is a sign of strength. But of course . . .' – here, he paused and looked up at the ceiling, clenching a fist and seeming to summon all his energies in order to hold on to the end of something large and powerful that was escaping – '. . . who is to say? . . . Why do people shout? To frighten others or to drown out their own fears?'

Ruth was struck by his voice, and then, as she continued listening, also by the way he unhurriedly crafted his speech, searching for balance and harmony with words he appeared to choose with care from among those that had the sharpest precision, that had sufficient size, greater weight. While he talked, at times taking a piece of chalk to illustrate an idea on the blackboard, she began inventing a life for him: he was the black sheep of a wealthy and ultra-conservative family – merchants, entrepreneurs; or per-haps the owners of a plantation, several factories, maybe even a shipyard – the sort of person relatives always low-ered their voices to discuss in stern or shocked tones after a dinner, when the time had come to smoke a last cigarette, the dishes had long been piled in the sink, and everyone thought the children already asleep.

A dozen or so metres from where she was piecing together her flight of fancy, Samuel suddenly drew one, two, three, four, five outlines on the blackboard.

'It's up to you,' he explained. 'You can have as many

puppets as you like. For all the authorities care, you can elect five representatives or two thousand. You know why? Because these positions are hollow. Because, in actual fact, your committee doesn't represent anything . . .'

He paused, for several seconds this time; casting his gaze over his audience, fixing them with the look of someone who has finally overcome the last obstacle or is about to strike the decisive blow: the blow that unhinges the door, fells the tree, sends the other boxer down.

'. . . more than a single person could represent . . .'

Then he crossed out the figures he had drawn earlier, one after the other, ensuring that in the heavy silence behind him they all clearly heard the rasp of the chalk drawing through each of the shapes, which now seemed suddenly superfluous, devoid of meaning.

'. . . Or if they prefer . . .'

He placed a palm on the blackboard.

'. . . the authorities could dismiss them at a single stroke!'

And with an abrupt sweep of his hand he effaced the heads of all the silhouettes.

The clarity of her memories made Ruth shiver again. She saw Samuel enter the room at the end of the corridor and started towards him, wondering if somewhere inside him, in a place she had yet to look, there remained something of that other man in the red shirt whom in some way she still loved; just as someone remembering a city still pictures a favourite square with geraniums on all the balconies and a pond in the centre and a row of acacias, though the square itself has long been demolished. And yet they continue to like it as much as before.

She opened the door. Took two steps into the room. 'How strange,' she thought, 'when I leave here, I'll no longer be Samuel's wife.'

'Look out, here comes the hound,' said Truman, in the living room from where he was watching ever more ominous clouds darken the intense blue of the sky. 'That's what they called it in El Salvador. Whenever they looked at the horizon and saw something heading their way, they'd say: "Here comes the hound."'

'And what did that mean?' asked Marta, without looking up from the magazine she was holding. 'That a storm was coming?'

'If you were lucky it was only a tropical storm. But sometimes it would be a tornado. Or a hurricane. And a hurricane could destroy buildings, tear down bridges, cause rivers to flood.'

Maceo was fascinated by his grandfather Truman's stories, by his memories of the years he spent abroad following the end of the Civil War. He often heard the same story more than once, but they both pretended not to notice – Maceo so he could listen to the story again and make it his own, his grandfather for the pleasure of telling it once more and the knowledge that it would never stop being his. At night, alone in his room, the boy could almost taste the names of all those far-off places: Panama, El Salvador, Costa Rica, Mexico.

'Is that where you went down inside the volcano?' he asked.

'Yes. The San Salvador volcano, in the capital. It was a frightening sight. It was so enormous that during the day you could see it from anywhere in the city.'

'. . . With its slopes covered in mango trees and its summit shrouded in mist,' concluded Marta. Neither Maceo nor Truman needed to look to know that a pitying or mocking smile played on her lips.

'Although long before that it had a different name,' continued Truman, ignoring her, 'Quezaltepec.'

'A long time before that?'

'At the time of the Maya. Did I ever tell you about the Maya Indians? They were the country's original inhabitants. They lived in Central America about 1,500 years ago. They were very intelligent: they built pyramids and saunas; they had an understanding of astronomy, and knew how to grow corn, tobacco, and maguey. And you know what?'

'What?'

'They loved dancing and made their drums from the shells of tortoises.'

Outside, the thunder clapped with such brute force that it shook the walls of the building. Had either of them been in the kitchen, they would have heard the cutlery rattle in its drawer.

'And what happened to the volcano after dark?'

'At night it disappeared, and then . . . well, then it became even more unsettling.'

'More unsettling?'

'Even though you couldn't see it, you could feel its presence; you knew it was out there, in the darkness.'

'Quezaltepec . . .' said Maceo.

Just then, there must have been a violent gust of wind, and for a few brief seconds they heard the metallic sound of the rain lashing the windows: a handful of small nails hurled against the glass.

'There was one storm in particular that I remember.' Truman's voice was now almost that of a man talking to himself. 'Lightning had struck a forest . . . trees were on fire . . . at each flash of lightning the volcano appeared for an instant, framed against the night sky. I kept remembering the time I had been inside it. To get there, remember, you had to follow the road through Santa Tecla; the entire crater was filled with orchids. I had never seen anything like it. White and purple orchids. Hundreds and hundreds of them.'

Marta let the magazine drop to her lap. She seemed annoyed. When the telephone began to ring, she went to answer it in the kitchen. Maceo and Truman heard her say: 'Have you looked outside? I just can't believe it. A lot of people think this has something to do with the comet.'

Maceo wondered if that was true. For the past two weeks people around him had spoken of nothing else: on television, newsreaders described the comet's speed, its size, how close it would pass to the Earth. Newspapers had published maps of the sky and photographs taken from space. Several television channels had shown documentaries about earthquakes and cyclones, and one of his teachers at school had explained that sixty-five million years ago it had been a meteorite that caused the extinction of the dinosaurs. He remembered that that particular meteorite had been ten kilometres wide; that it fell in the Yucatán Peninsula in Mexico; and that it consisted of the minerals chromium-53 and iridium. If he closed his eyes he could hear again and again the incredible story their teacher had told them, her measured yet captivating voice saying: 'The meteorite's impact filled the Earth's atmos-phere with ash which hid the sun for months, perhaps years. It caused five-kilometre-high waves, fires raged through the forests, and acid rain began to fall on the Earth.'

'I can still see it all now,' Truman continued, 'it's so unbe-

13

lievably clear. Not that it makes it any easier to . . . well, it's as if the years hadn't gone by, and yet they have. As if *now* was still *then* and what we call *now* was only a dream. One morning we went to the waterfalls in Panchimalco, because Cecilia's father had bought her a car and we . . . It was a Ford, with white tyres, and to me the sound those tyres made was different from that of other tyres – as if they weren't rotating but gliding. Silly, isn't it? Have I ever mentioned Cecilia to you before? She was so perfect that a friend of ours used to call her "the Isosceles Woman". Another day we went to the Lake of Ilopango. The lava peaks there all had names like the Hill of Monkeys, the Island of Ducks. Why not? They were just part of the . . . landscape . . .'

Truman's eyes were slowly closing. He recognised the symptoms: first, the feeling that he was sinking in snow; then a sensation of heaviness lasting for the fifteen or so seconds that preceded sleep. He still managed to say:

'It was only to be with her that I went to El Salvador.'

It seemed, however, that Maceo was no longer listening; that he was still thinking about the meteorite, about the dinosaurs lying dead on beaches, along river banks, amid the cinders of smouldering forests. He wondered if the comet expected to pass the Earth in several days' time would cause a similar event to happen. He looked out at the storm, at the sombre afternoon and was then overcome by a sense of foreboding. Had he been old enough to find the words to express what he felt, he would have thought: 'It's everywhere you go – there's no place on Earth you can hide from the sky.' But he was still too young, which meant he would not spend the rest of his life telling everyone the story of how he once saw into the future.

'You may not believe this,' he would have said, 'but ten minutes before it happened, I had already seen it.'

14

III

'Who the hell are you trying to fool? You or me?'

Until that point in the conversation Samuel had kept his back turned to Ruth and paid little attention to what she was saying, while he undressed – his usual sequence: tie–trousers–jacket–jumper–shirt – facing the balcony and staring out at the red buses, deserted shops, and streaming pavements, not noticing that the air in the room had become charged and volatile. But on saying this, he turned to confront her with the suddenness of a trapped animal.

'You don't understand,' Ruth said. 'It's a waste of time, because you don't want to understand. Our only option . . .'

'Excuse me, but in this family the words *our* and *option* are incompatible. You can choose, I can't. Instead, I have to spend half my life earning enough for us to get by.'

'*You* have to? And what about my . . .'

'What about what you earn? I wish that could pay the mortgage, the school fees, the insurance, Marta's course.'

'You're overlooking something. I don't . . .' Ruth began to feel exposed, unable to plug the holes Samuel was making below her waterline. She began to feel the discouragement that came when no one understood, when best intentions were misconstrued or came to nothing; but also the resentment at ceding ground, allowing the enemy to advance without being able to strike back.

'. . . Why do you always have to twist every word I say, confuse everything. Anyway, that's not what we were discussing.'

15

'Isn't it? Let's see now: I get back from the office at six, in other words, after spending about nine hours away from home; I come in here to get changed; my wife follows me into the room and I think to myself, now she'll say, "Welcome home. How was work? What would you like for dinner?"'

'Listen, Samuel, this has all gone too far and it's already very . . .'

'. . . but instead, you come in here and ask: "Why did you unplug the television? Why did you switch all the lights off in the other rooms? Why did you become a different man?" And then stand there staring at me as if I were some kind of . . . some kind of . . . I'm sure you know better than me what I look like.'

'I do – especially when you decide to change into those ridiculous pyjamas.'

Samuel looked down at what he was wearing. She was right – he had just put on his pyjamas. Suddenly it struck him that there was something inexplicable about that combination of yellow cloth, violet stripes, and white plastic buttons.

'Ridiculous? Have you gone completely mad? These were a present from you!'

'And here we are, living over a butcher's.'

Seen from outside, for example from the windows of the building opposite, Samuel and Ruth must have seemed indistinct and rigid, perhaps a little ungainly, like toy soldiers moved by the hand of a child. Such a distance – those twenty-five or thirty metres that the rain and the daylight's underwater gloom had transformed into an unreal, almost opaque space – made it impossible to sense the similarities between their marriage and the storm, or to note the evident signs of the collapse, mud, ashes, and ruins to come.

From closer to, however, from inside the room itself, it was easy to discern in the dirty gleam of her pupils or in the twitch of her lips – a downwards turn, a slight tremor – that she was starting to feel the approach of tears, to taste the bitter juice rising inexorably up from her stomach all the way to her eyes without being able to put up her defences, check its advance. It was clear, too, that some kind of alarm had been triggered inside Samuel, an emergency signal warning him that the ground underfoot was no longer safe, that he was standing on the edge of an abyss, was about to step on shifting sands.

'What man?' he said, eventually. 'What kind of man have I become? What are you trying to say? What are you accusing me of? Am I irresponsible or selfish or lazy?'

A van stopped in the street below their balcony and for a few moments, unable to say anything more, unable to extricate themselves from their web of words, they caught the sound of the rain falling on the roof of the vehicle. Samuel pictured the driver: an overweight man in his fifties, dressed in a no-doubt grey tracksuit, who, as he waited for the traffic light to turn green, rested his hand on the gear stick, such that the vibrations of the engine sent a mechanical pulse right through his body as though he, too, were made of pistons, fan belt, valves, and ball bearings. Ruth, for some reason, imagined the van to be loaded with crates of fish.

'A man who removes the bulbs from half the lights,' Ruth said, 'who thinks that banks steal his money, that restaurants cheat him, that garages fit his car with used parts.'

'The light bulbs? But you know how important it is not to waste energy. And you can't deny that some restaurants . . .'

Ruth put her face in her hands, and burst into tears. She was crying for herself, for Marta and Maceo, for the scarlet-shirted young man that Samuel used to be, for the way her dreams had turned out to be nothing more than dreams.

In recent nights, after tossing and turning in bed or getting up to watch television or warm some milk in the kitchen – only to then spend ten, fifteen, twenty minutes staring at the untouched glass before her, perhaps trying to see the link between her own life and the way the white liquid, without apparent or visible change, was slowly cooling – an incident from her childhood repeatedly came to mind. The incident happened in the seventies, when her family lived in Bilbao, in an apartment block in Calle Cosme Echebarrieta. One Friday in August, her parents told her they were planning to take her the next day to see a travelling circus. Ruth still remembered how she spent the morning staring at the brightly coloured brochure that announced the various acts; how she then started imagining the size and smell of the animals, and even looked at a map of India in the atlas to see where the fakir came from. So that when the following afternoon finally arrived, and the family gradually left behind the known, seemingly accessible world of the Escolapios College in Calle Espartero, of the sports club in Alameda de Recalde, of the fountain and local government offices in Plaza Elíptica; as they approached the big top erected in Avenida Basurto and walked along the Gran Vía or past the Museum of Fine Arts, glimpsing between every second building a section of the Doña Casilda Park, or in the distance, the Statue of the Sacred Heart; as they reached the Avenida de José Antonio Primo de Rivera and saw the walls of the San Mamés Stadium, all those exotic names – New Delhi, Bombay, the Ganges, Calcutta – were spinning inside her head, sparkling like precious stones, giving off an aroma of rare spices.

The show, however, left her with a feeling of sadness: the trapeze artists had worn faded leotards, the lion tamer a crumpled frock coat, the human rocket an outfit designed for a shorter, thinner man; the three lions were either too old or had been sedated; and the fakir who swallowed sabres and torches in front of the half-empty spectator stands had worn olive-green make-up so as to appear Hindu – even though he was in fact a Spaniard from Galicia whom they had spotted on arrival, by the ticket booth, already wearing his turban and nervously smoking a Rex. He had surveyed the brief line of families waiting to buy tickets and said to the girl behind the counter:

'Reckon I should've stayed in bed, my girl. Show's hardly worth it for this lot.'

Ruth almost forgot about the circus until a week later, when at breakfast – hot chocolate, sweet buns, fruit juice – her mother read out a newspaper article about how one of the lions had been abandoned on the outskirts of the city, after the show. It had been left in a steel cage in the shade of trees; the article went on to say that the owners of the circus were almost certainly bankrupt, that they lacked the means to feed all the animals, hence the abandoned lion; at the time of writing, neighbours were keeping the animal alive by feeding it bits of food and leftovers from their own meals.

After school on the Monday, her father took her – by car, this time – to where the big top had been erected in the Avenida de José Antonio y Basurto a few days earlier; and from there, drove to an area of open ground where they soon found what they had come to see. A small crowd stood around the cage, inside which was the lion, surrounded by heaps of scraps. People were throwing it bones, raw meat, tinned food, even pieces of sandwich.

They would stay for a while, in silence, before walking off, gravely shaking their heads and looking sorrowful, as if they had just learnt an awful truth about their own fates.

Now, thirty years later, standing before the man she was about to leave for ever, Ruth no longer knew quite why she still remembered that childhood episode; why, night after night, as she sat in the darkened kitchen preparing the words to say goodbye to Samuel, images came to mind, not only of the main characters in the story – her father, the fakir, the lion, herself – but also half a dozen absurd details about strangers, such as the woman in gumboots or the two girls who each wore the same pale-coloured overcoat, in a shade between ochre and fried egg yolk.

Nor did she know how her conversation with Samuel had departed from its intended course, how the words she so carefully prepared on her own had led to the usual arguments over wastefulness, saving electricity, bills, the children, how tired they both felt; how her words became like a smouldering pile of dead leaves slowly and need-lessly sending its smoke back in their faces.

'I've always done the best I could for all of you,' he said. 'I've had to make numerous sacrifices.'

'Maybe. But you weren't him. You cheated me. You weren't the boy I met.'

'Who? What are you talking about?'

'And it's not true you've made sacrifices. That's another lie. All you ever gave up is what you weren't.'

'I haven't made any sacrifices?'

'I . . .' Ruth began. 'I can't continue to . . .' but here she stopped. Talking seemed useless, even harmful; every word left them feeling slightly more alone. Or maybe the opposite was true, and what she needed was to find just one more word, a verb or noun as powerful and deadly as a virus, a word able to penetrate the silence, infect it, and make it disappear.

'Well, then . . . What's going on? What's changed? All of a sudden you . . .'

Samuel took a step towards her, but as if she were now on a boat about to set sail; he reached out and touched her shoulder with his fingertips – her skin felt as cold as a gun. It was then that Ruth knew the moment had come. The moment to draw on the long list of wrongs, humiliations, petty acts and injustices which for so many years each had committed against the other and which they both pretended to forget, though these all remained as hidden scars, as open secrets, as ammunition stockpiled in preparation for war. And perhaps the moment had also come to tell him about the other man.

'Now listen, Samuel . . .'

But she had to stop there, for at that instant, with a violence akin to the blows of the meat cleaver downstairs, Marta flung open the door. Though she did not say a word, the shock showing in her eyes told them both that something awful had happened.

IV

At the age of eleven, Maceo was not really sure what death meant, but already it frightened him. He may have been too young to lie awake at night tormented by notions such as *illness* or *pain*, but he did fear death with a kind of blind awareness, with that abstract yet unerring insight that led a child to see from the outset something fatal about a world that contained words like *gravedigger*, *tombstone*, and *coffin*. And one of the things that frightened him was the way Truman would fall asleep like that, in mid-sentence, letting an object drop to the floor – a pencil, an apple – and then lie there, mouth half-open, his face suddenly slack, expressionless, deserted.

So that afternoon, when he had stopped thinking about dinosaurs and meteorites, he went over to his grandfather and placed a hand on his heart to see if it was still beating. If he was dead, Maceo intended to become a scientist and bring him back to life; it would mean spending years locked away in his laboratory, years of erroneous equations and wasted days, afternoons when he would lose all track of time; it would mean working without knowing whether it was day or night, leaving trays of food forgotten on a table, pausing only to empty an ashtray and smoke yet another cigarette as he pursued his experiments on rats, birds, frogs. He saw himself cut open one of these small bodies, separate muscle from tissue, cut through bones and organs to the heart, which beat, then stopped; he stared, knowing that it concealed the biggest secret of all, that there had to be a way to stop and start it at will. Yet progress was so slow and confusing, so many avenues of investigation led nowhere. Despite his exhaustion, he collected a bag from the kitchen and left the building; except for road sweepers, the streets were empty as he wandered deserted districts of the city in search of living specimens – there were always stray cats to be found prowling the alleys or lurking among the bins at the back of restaurants. Suddenly he heard a noise coming from behind a pile of crates: it was not a cat but a man, probably a beggar. Maceo remembered Truman, whose body lay frozen inside a special chamber awaiting his breakthrough. He glanced over his shoulder, then started walking silently towards the man.

Meanwhile, Marta was still on the telephone. On the other end of the line someone was telling her about a boy called Lucas, and although from Ruth and Samuel's kitchen we naturally cannot hear what this person was saying, it is easy to imagine it in part when we hear this side of the conversation:

'Lucas? I don't believe it. I'm telling you – Luisa always detested him. One day Lucas and I were talking about her . . . I think there must be some mistake.'

'. . . / . . .'

'Are you sure?'

'. . . / . . .'

'Yes, well, maybe that doesn't bother him. But I'm not so sure . . . or maybe he hasn't seen that side of her yet.' Despite her efforts to sound disinterested, she was unable to stop the shockwaves spreading through her body, numbing her mind like an anaesthetic.

'. . . / . . .'

'He's certainly good-looking, the swine. He looks like

23

he's stepped straight out of an advert. Anyway, good luck to her, I say. Perhaps she doesn't care. If you're going to get stabbed, it may as well be with a beautiful blade.'

'. . . / . . .'

'Maybe. But don't start believing everything you hear. You know how much people like to . . .'

'. . . / . . .'

'OK. But that doesn't mean . . .'

'. . . / . . .'

'Really? She was in the car with him? So they *were* actually together at some point. But I still . . .'

'. . . / . . .'

'Well, in that case, I'm the one who's wrong.' Marta closed her eyes, pressing her fingertips to her temples and shaking her head in silent disbelief. She turned to the wall, biting her lips, and began tracing a path with her nail along the gaps between the tiles.

'. . . / . . .'

'They're having a party at a house in the country? No. I didn't know his parents had a house in the country. No, he never told me.'

'. . . / . . .'

'Yes. It'll be all covered in snow. Anyway, woods give me the creeps.' She remembered how when she was small the family occasionally went for Sunday walks up in the hills, and how Truman once told her that eating fresh snow purified the blood, which made her try it. Why was she remembering that now? What had the snow tasted of? She hadn't known then, but she did now: it tasted of loneliness, of despair, of emptiness.

'. . . / . . .'

'Perhaps you're right, but I don't trust animals unless they're cooked.' She tried once more to pretend that she

24

was still in one piece, though she knew her whole world was falling apart, reverting to what it had always been – a place where a cellar was just a cellar, a car just a car, and a cinema no more than a cinema. She could see the magic disappearing, the way a lover watching their partner slowly getting dressed by the bed sees each additional item of clothing remove another part of the naked body, until the other person emerges, the ordinary mortal, a human being the same as anyone else.

'... / ...'

'Anyway, what do we care? Let the two of them celebrate on their own.' Her vision blurred, the words choked in her throat, and for several seconds – during which she kept her hand over the mouthpiece – she had the sensation of being off balance, as when a tread of the stairs gives way underfoot.

'... / ...'

'Yes, I could take it along. I've also bought the Oasis album. In any case, I don't think I'll be going.'

'... / ...'

'2,200 pesetas. That's what I paid. That's ... what ...' – now she was hardly able to suppress a sob – 'almost all CDs cost these days.'

'... / ...'

'No, I already had the Beck.'

'... / ...'

'Of course, I'm fine.'

'... / ...'

'What do I think? I think they can go to hell.'

They went on talking like this for a long time. Marta was now sitting on a stool in the kitchen, staring blankly at the floor as her mind reviewed a sequence of images of the Lucas in question: queuing alongside her outside a cinema, vowing eternal love as he kissed her or undid her bra in the back row. Although if it is literally true that a state of mind can transport a person, Marta doubtless now found herself in another part of the world – in a place where the winters were long and cold and the roads icy; a place where at night families needed weapons to ward off the wolves. One afternoon, on her way home from doing some shopping, her van had broken down by the lake, in the middle of some woods.

She had passed that way once before – a few months earlier, when the weather had been a little warmer – to watch people fishing for an animal called a silurid. It had been the opening of the fishing season, and she had been told to expect a lively occasion: at midnight, everyone would gather round the campfire to sing folk songs and eat a small piece of the best catch of the day, a custom said to bring luck in the coming year. But Marta found the whole spectacle revolting: the women talking in loud voices by the bonfires; the men drinking cheap wine; the monstrous silurids – with their long scaleless bodies the colour of oil, their gigantic whiskers, their glutinous sheen – expiring inside a large bin.

That had been her last visit to the area; since then, she had always crossed the woods as quickly as she could, and out of superstition avoided even glancing at the lake or the river. Hence when her van broke down in that particular spot she at once fell prey to an irrational fear. At first she tried deluding herself by locking all the doors and nonchalantly smoking a cigarette: the engine had overheated, she should have noticed it earlier, it would start again in five minutes and she'd be on her way home. But when she turned the key nothing happened, and all around the silence persisted.

Darkness was descending from the trees, and in the distance she could hear the sound of the river. The darkness reminded her of the wolves and the river, of the silurids. She knew that wolves came down from the mountains in packs of seven or eight. Silurids lived in deep water and hunted along the beds of rivers at night; they spent the winters not eating, drowsy until spring. She began to blow the horn. No one heard. She blew it two, three, four, five, ten, twenty times, jabbing hysterically, but the sound grew weaker and weaker as the battery ran down, until in the end it gave out, leaving her all alone with her fear and a voice saying: 'Stay here, and you'll freeze to death. Step out of the car, and the wolves will kill you. You'll end up at the bottom of the river or the lake, devoured by the silurids.'

That was the kind of place and situation in which the girl now found herself, even as she sat in Ruth and Samuel's kitchen seeing how the storm appeared to have abated, despite the occasional rumble of thunder and odd flash of lightning over the rooftops. The darkness of the afternoon had spread, casting the room into shadow and lending objects – a pair of cups, a bottle of milk, a pan – a rusted sheen, as though sunk on a seabed.

'Lucas . . .' she murmured. 'I don't believe it. It must be a mistake. Not Lucas and Luisa.'

How strange to hear the combination of those two names, which to her sounded as incompatible and as much at odds as *hot* and *cold*, *happy* and *sad*, *life* and *death*.

In the living room, Maceo was looking at the front page of the newspaper. It showed a picture of the comet, next to an article about its age, orbit, and core of solid ice. The article compared it to other comets and listed their names: Halley, Kohoutek, West, Brooks, Encke.

He went over to the windows. The rain had almost ceased, and now the street appeared as dark and still as a large magnet. He went out onto the balcony: he wanted to stare at the sky, in search of stars, meteorites, satellites. He placed his hands on the railing and looked up. And it was then that he guessed, a second before it happened; it was then that he knew for certain something was hurtling towards him. Instinctively, he tried to let go of the metal railing, but already it was too late.

From the kitchen, Marta saw him thrown to the ground. She saw the lightning reach down from the clouds and strike the balcony, she heard the shocking sound of the electrical discharge, and when she heard the thunder, she started to run.

The same crash of thunder woke Truman, but he was unsure from whence it came – whether from this side of sleep or the other.

Ruth and Samuel stared at Marta standing in the doorway, her face disfigured by panic and tears, as she said: 'Lightning! Oh my God, I saw it! He was on the balcony! He was . . . Maceo's been killed by lightning!'

In the kitchen, the receiver hung where she had dropped it, twirling in mid-air. A voice inside it was saying: 'Marta? Are you there? Can you hear me, Marta? Are you sure you're OK? Is anybody there? Marta?'

But no one answered those words, which now seemed to struggle amongst themselves, spinning and disappearing for ever, like drowned insects swirled down the plughole of a bath.

CHAPTER TWO

However, Marta was wrong, and whilst the lightning doubtless killed many things, fortunately Maceo was not one of them.

Despite all that had happened, at this very moment, when the boy had been in hospital and out of danger for the past three or four hours, resting in bed after undergoing a series of blood tests, X-rays, and scans of his heart and brain, his entire family continued to picture him lying, as if dead, on the balcony, shoeless, his clothes in shreds. He was not dead, but that was the image of him that remained, for fear has its own, often illogical rules: inside the man dreaming of a leopard, roams a leopard; in every dark, empty cellar lurks an assassin.

Samuel was only two blocks away from their apartment, in the hospital cafeteria, a place he knew well, and from where he now endlessly recalled the moment they had found Maceo, head thrown back, eyes sunken, legs splayed at an odd angle, as if dislocated or forced apart. From time to time, as he sipped a beer or had a snack, slightly guilty at the gratifying taste of the alcohol or food which he somehow sensed was incompatible with the concern he felt for Maceo, Samuel would also see himself in the street, running in the rain with his son in his arms, rushing for two blocks, shouldering aside those in his path, feeling his muscles become tenser and tenser, fearing they would snap and that he would never reach the casualty department. For no reason he could explain, he remembered all this as seen from above, as if filmed from a helicopter.

Until that night, Samuel had always liked the hospital cafeteria. He often went there, both during the week and at weekends, when he went out to buy a newspaper or was on his way home from the office. It was a place he preferred to other bars and cafés; he felt at ease among the small gathering of individuals who usually sat alone and rarely spoke – people able to share the outside world with that other world of operating theatres and doctors, patients and nurses; people apparently adaptable and resilient enough to live in two such different environments.

In the course of these visits – for breakfast, or at times an afternoon coffee – Samuel had taken to observing the mostly glum and weary people who sat there, lost in thought. There were always pale, badly shaven men, and women who wore the same slippers and cardigans they doubtless wore at home; all ate whatever was on offer, hardly looking up from their plates, before they ordered a tea or glass of milk or slice of cake 'to go', and disappeared back to their rooms, back to their family tragedies.

By counting the number of weeks for which he saw a certain individual, Samuel could get an approximate idea of the gravity of their relative's condition. What he had never stopped to consider, though, was that the day would eventually come when he would no longer be a spectator but a participant; when he would find himself in their shoes, pondering a thousand bewildering questions as he ate a sandwich or drank a beer.

He remembered the time a couple of boys had come in to ask for two cans of Coca-Cola and some sandwiches. The waiter had placed the drinks on the counter and called back to his colleague in the kitchen: 'Two *emparedados* to go – one vegetable, one mixed!'

'*Emparedados*? Listen,' said one of the boys, 'what we want are sandwiches.'

'Fine. It's just that here we call them *emparedados*.'

'You're joking . . .' The pair had started to smile. 'What do you make them with?'

'We make them', interrupted the waiter as brusquely as he could, 'with regular sliced bread.'

The boys exchanged a complicitous look. Samuel guessed that they were students.

'Look,' said the taller of the two, 'it's just that an *emparedado*[*] doesn't sound like a sandwich.'

'Oh, really? So what does it sound like?'

'It sounds like . . . well, I'd say it sounds like an insurance salesman who's been buried in the cellar by his wife,' one of the boys replied, and several customers started to laugh.

'That's right,' said the other, and added what must have been a private joke, 'and I'd say he was Belgian. A Belgian insurance salesman. Like Julio Cortázar.'

That day, Samuel had been one of those who laughed along with the rest; but on this occasion – and without realising it – he had the same reaction as a woman who'd been sitting at the back of the cafeteria whose sister lay dying from cancer in an intensive-care ward on the third floor. First, he imagined that man sitting in the poorly lit kitchen of an old house, not tasting the poison in his soup; he then imagined the same man as a corpse, with blue hands, buried upright in the wall of the garage, still wearing his hat and overcoat. Samuel thought that if he ever put his mind to it, he'd certainly be able to recognise the smell of arsenic and fresh cement.

[*]The word for a sandwich of this kind (made with sliced bread rather than a baguette) can literally mean 'immured' or 'hidden between two walls'. (Translator's Note)

In the west wing of the building, Ruth was sitting on a cream-coloured chair by Maceo's bedside. The boy was asleep and the coin-operated television had just switched itself off, so now the room was in complete silence.

Ruth felt anxious; she paced uneasily from one side of the room to the other, sensing she lacked the strength to come to terms with her surroundings. The institutional cleanliness, the smell of medication, the walls painted in an oppressive tone of white – all combined to make her feel sick, for they probably seemed part of her bad luck, part of the misfortune that had befallen her son.

From time to time she glanced through a magazine or newspaper, turned on the radio or went to the window to search the sky for any sign of the meteorite storm mentioned in the newspaper. She had read that cosmic rain visible to the naked eye would appear between midnight and 3 a.m. in the vicinity of the constellation of Leo. It comprised the remains of the star of the Temple-Turttle comet and was expected to enter the Earth's atmosphere as bullet-sized fragments travelling at a speed of seventy kilometres per second, at the quantity of 140,000 fragments per hour. Astronomers had predicted possible damage to satellites, and that many people could experience interruptions to their mobile telephone and satellite dish signals. But however much she looked, she could see nothing, save for a night as black and empty as hell itself.

At other times, after checking Maceo's temperature or adjusting his bed sheets, she would sit in the armchair, close her eyes, and for a few minutes try to distract herself by remembering episodes from her past; until, all of a sudden, a tiny detail would cause her unease and anguish to return; her worst fears to close in like dogs gaining on an escaped prisoner.

For instance, she remembered an accident that occurred in Bilbao, in the days when she was still at school: a tanker carrying petrol had overturned by the river, and its entire load – about 40,000 litres of aviation fuel destined for the airport – had spilled into the water. The stain remained there for a week. Aviation fuel, her father told her, was dangerous, and inflammable in the extreme. They heard on the radio that the pollution had killed all the fish; that flocks of hungry seagulls were starting to be seen in the city, where they were drawn to gardens, dustbins, and kitchen windows in search of scraps. The announcer had added that the seagulls would soon be attacking the weakest members of the community – the elderly, babies in parks, children in playgrounds.

'Jesus, Mary and Joseph! This fool thinks he's Alfred Hitchcock.'

Ruth smiled as she heard the voice of her father, who had died three years earlier; she remembered his penchant for expressions like 'Jesus, Mary and Joseph', 'fool', and 'inflammable *in the extreme*'. Then, without warning, the petrol stain, the dead fish, and the hungry seagulls appeared to her to be dangerous precedents, deadly warnings. She went again to feel Maceo's forehead and check that his breathing was regular. He was fine. His skin was so delicate and pale that in places – the eyelids, the temples – it seemed almost transparent.

She gazed again at the sky. There was no sign of the star storm – only ordinary, unswerving, incessant rain.

Naturally, she had not forgotten her conversation with Samuel, the manner in which it had got out of hand. She remembered the other man. And felt ashamed. Samuel was mediocre and small-minded, but he was also decent and loyal. The other man's name was Ramón. She returned her attention to the newspaper and learnt that the sea horse was in danger of extinction, that over twenty million specimens were caught every year; in Hong Kong it was sold stuffed; in China it was used in ointments and pills; in many parts of Asia it was eaten fried. Like the chameleon, the sea horse had the ability to change colour and could turn spectacular fluorescent hues in order to mimic its surroundings or express emotions; it was also said to be a cure for asthma and thyroid problems; its mating ritual was very beautiful.

'God help us,' Ruth said. 'God help us all.'

II

'On Saturdays they went to the Parque Central, right opposite the Metropolitan Cathedral; the boys would stand on one side and the girls on the other. You know, so that they could choose partners. And then they'd go dancing in one of the ballrooms of the Gran Hotel.'

'Were there many Spaniards?' asked Maceo. He was propped up in his hospital bed, still feeling that almost liquid drowsiness that comes from spending several days lying down, on medication, and sleeping at odd hours of the day and night.

'There were Catalans and Canary Islanders,' Truman said, 'who owned shops like La Gloria and El Globo. I often went down that way, to the Central Market, where you'd find everything from shoemakers to tailors. There was the Solera pharmacy, the San Juan de Dios clinic, the El Cometa bakery . . . Yes, there were plenty of Spaniards. In fact, the Solera pharmacy belonged to the father of one of my best friends, Juan Garcés, who was from Las Palmas.'

'Costa Rica was where you met that woman? Or was that in El Salvador?'

'You mean Cecilia? Yes, that was in Costa Rica – December, 1938. In the capital, San José. As it happens, I was with Garcés that day.'

'What were the Spaniards doing in San José? Did you find work?'

'No. That came a few years later, in Panama. But in Costa Rica I had no worries – I had brought money with me from Spain and was happy to spend it. I was very young. At an age when you need distractions and don't yet know how to make plans for the future; when you won't settle for just keeping your head above water; when you think that the opposite of swimming is sinking.'

'And that's not true.'

'Yes. Yes, it is. But not always.'

Maceo wondered how something could be a lie and at the same time not be a lie.

'So', he said, 'that was when you were twenty . . .'

'Nineteen. Only nineteen.'

'. . . and had that money.'

'As soon as I arrived, I changed all my money into the local currency, colóns, and deposited it in a bank. Many Spaniards kept their pesetas, not wanting to part with Spanish money; some saved as much as they could and even went hungry, skimping on food and clothing when there was no need to, in the belief that better times would come when we eventually won the war; others hid wads of Spanish banknotes anywhere they could – in drawers with secret compartments, under floor tiles. And you know what happened?'

'It was stolen.'

'No. Well, maybe it was, in a certain sense. Yes, it was stolen, though it wasn't taken away from them.'

'How?'

'It was money issued by the Republic, and so after Franco won, it became worthless: it was no longer legal tender, not even worth the paper it was printed on. Can you imagine what that meant? From one day to the next, all those people who thought they had a small fortune had lost everything; suddenly they found themselves in serious trouble, bankrupt.'

'But that didn't happen to you. You were lucky.'

'I was, and so were all the others who had adapted to the life of that country. We had made friends with the local people right from the start. Many Spaniards only socialised amongst themselves – which was a way of keeping their distance. They lived alongside the locals, but never *with* them. They were always talking about Barcelona, Tenerife, Las Palmas; they bought local produce but only to cook Spanish dishes. But my friends and I were young, we wanted to have fun, live life to the full. On Saturdays we went to those dances at the Gran Hotel. We drank Los Negritos and Imperial beer, and at parties a drink called *guaro*, which was distilled from sugar cane. The last thing we wanted to hear about was paellas or *escaldones*. We loved Costa Rican food – the meat stews, the soups made from vegetables with wonderful names like *challote*, *yuca*, *tiquisque*, and *camote*, which looked like a yam or sweet potato. And a dish made with beans and rice, called *gallopinto*.'

The exotic names had a soothing effect on Maceo, and he enjoyed that particular story as much as all the others. He had been in hospital for three days and would have liked to stay longer, but he was to be discharged the following morning.

'What about Cecilia?' he asked.

'That was a little later, on the beach at Puntarenas.'

'Is that where you all went to swim?'

'Not really. There was another dance hall there, called Los Baños, in the Hotel Tioga where rich people sometimes spent the weekend.'

'Rich people didn't mix with poor people?'

'Not much. In fact, you could almost say they had their own San José – a city within the city, but separate. They lived in their mansions in the Amón district; on Saturdays they sometimes took the train to Puntarenas on the Pacific Ocean, and the rest of the time, Monday to Friday, they would spend the mornings on their plantations, overseeing their banana and coffee crops, and the afternoons at the Club Unión, which was a cross between a restaurant and a casino.'

'But you met Cecilia on the beach.'

'I met her at that Los Baños dance hall. I had spent the day in Cartago with some friends. It had been a wonderful trip – we'd passed through plantations and coffee fields, seen the Irazú volcano, as well as the ruins of the old cathedral that had been destroyed twice by earthquakes.'

'Twice?'

'That's right. Twice. The story goes that it was God's punishment for the death of a priest who'd been killed inside the cathedral.'

'Someone killed him?'

'Yes. To steal the alms money.'

'And God destroyed the cathedral.' Suddenly the boy's eyelids began to droop; he sensed the ceiling, the light, the walls, and the cream-coloured chair all changing size and shape, becoming ever smaller and less distinct, as if he were seeing them from the window of a retreating car or train.

'The first time it happened, no one wanted to believe it,' Truman went on, 'but after the second earthquake, they gave up. They abandoned the old church and built a new one, the Basilica of Our Lady of the Angels, five hundred metres further along. Anyway, that was the sort of thing I knew about in those days. You see, I'd fallen in love with that country, with its smell, its traditions, its wonderful food. And the moment I saw her, the moment I saw Cecilia dancing . . . It was as if all those things had come together

40

and assumed the form of a woman. Shall I tell you what she looked like?' Truman asked. But when he looked across at Maceo, he saw that the boy had fallen asleep.

'How unlucky,' he thought, 'to be struck by lightning. Or maybe not – maybe I should see it the other way round and think how lucky you are to have something like that happen to you and still be alive. Besides, what could you have done? Nothing – nothing at all. That's the trouble with life: you can't make things not happen.'

III

'Fools may laugh, but a thorn can kill. They seem harmless when you get one in your palm or fingertip, but ignore them, and they'll pass up your veins to your heart and stab you like a knife.'

Marta typed the words *sulphur* and *blue flame*. Then she paused, and stared blankly at the typewriter. She was at the secretarial college when she suddenly remembered her father telling her this, one St Valentine's Day, next to a vase full of roses, as he used a needle to remove a tiny thorn from her finger. She hated Samuel for having forced her to attend the college, for the persistence with which he had insisted she combine her medical studies with lessons in typing and shorthand, saying that if all else failed and she couldn't find a job after she graduated, at least she would have something secure to fall back on, an ace up her sleeve, a starting point.

'Security!' she had repeated loudly at dinner, one evening three months earlier. 'You think being a secretary guarantees you security?'

'Two hundred words a minute', replied Samuel, 'is security.'

'No, it isn't, not when you don't need it.'

'Really? What makes you so sure? Don't belittle it just yet. It may one day prove to be your last resort.'

'I'm studying medicine. Or maybe that slipped your mind. You know – to become a doctor. I won't be needing a last resort.'

'You don't think so? Why, then, are so many people unemployed?'

'That won't concern me as soon as I know the difference between fusiform and orbicular muscles, between the deltoid and the trapezius, the sartorius and the sternomastoid.'

'Fine. I admit that's the main part, the most important thing. But it's not everything.'

'Dad! In the past, you were always telling me . . .' But Samuel cut her off, raising a hand to indicate that was the end of the matter, that there was nothing more to discuss.

Just then Ruth gave an inexplicable little laugh, and the two of them looked across at her in surprise. They would never have guessed that she had just heard her father exclaim: 'Goodness me! This fellow's no optimist!' Samuel stared at Ruth for a second, his eyes burning with hatred. Then he turned back to his daughter.

'A little humility, Marta. That's all I'm asking of you. Don't lose sight of your ambitions, but learn to be a little more humble.'

As she peered down into her soup, Marta saw a dim office with grey plastic blinds on the windows, a desk littered with paperwork and files, a broken fan. Her boss was called Señor Romero or perhaps Señor Gutiérrez. He was a cowardly, lazy, rude, and corrupt individual – a corporal or policeman, at heart – shamelessly docile with his superiors, childishly overbearing with subordinates, as sly as a fox and as slow as a mule. Every morning, at around half past eight or quarter to nine, Marta would arrive for work at that bastard's office, wearing a salmon-pink acrylic dress, a checked shirt, a striped sweater and suede jacket, or a purple jacket over a yellow, white or sky-blue skirt. She would certainly be holding a cup of coffee.

43

Despite her protestations, Samuel had enrolled her at the secretarial college. At first, Marta attended twice a week, did the class exercises, and went straight home. Then, as the weeks passed, she began to spend these Wednesday and Friday afternoons with Lucas. Seeing him at such times allowed Marta to feel a sense of impunity – as far as the rest of the world was concerned, she was sitting on an adjustable office chair learning to touch-type the alphabet on an old Olivetti, and thus her moments with Lucas did not really exist: she never was in that bar, or shopping centre, or cinema; instead, she was in a classroom taking notes on her pad, and when Lucas undid a zip, pulled down a strap, or took hold of her hand, she was elsewhere, taking dictation.

Her feelings for Lucas were strong but confused. She was entranced by his good looks and muscular body, by his impetuous nature and the cruel yet sweet way he had of sneering at things, as if their importance could only ever be relative. These, however, were also the very same factors that led Marta to fear him, to see him as potentially dangerous and unstable, and thus her heart and mind were filled with a confusing array of certainties and suspicions. She knew that he desired her, and at times in a way that was feverish, even extreme. But was desire, she wondered, a proof of love or a form of selfishness? Every time she was with Lucas he wanted more and more, but what would happen when she had given him everything? Was his audacity a sign of loyalty – *I'll never tire of you, I'll love you for ever* – or simply impatience?

It was clear that the telephone conversation on the day Maceo was struck by lightning made the latter seem more likely. On reflection, though, was it really as clear as that? Why? Was it true what they had told her? Perhaps it was all a mistake, a slight on his character, a simple misunder-

44

standing? Had Lucas really been in a car with a girl called Luisa? Had someone actually seen them entering a hotel?

Marta glanced towards the street, at the dirty rooftops and cloudy sky. The comet was expected in two days' time and many saw it as a sign of impending disaster. The news bulletins were already reporting an international cold spell, with temperatures still falling, and a total of 130 victims in Europe alone. She recalled the television images: cars buried in the snow somewhere in Romania; people running in a Prague street; the Danube frozen over in Budapest. She returned her attention to the book open in front of her and went on copying: '. . . *is one of the constituents of gunpowder*'. She stopped. The Olivetti typewriter suddenly seemed an extraordinary piece of equipment. Her brother lay in hospital. She typed: '. . . *is mixed with salt-petre and carbon*'. Each stroke of the typewriter sounded like . . . like what exactly? Like a man banging nails into a coffin? Soldiers shooting at an empty can?

'I will go to the party at Lucas's house,' she thought to herself. 'I'll show them all who they're dealing with. It'll be an ambush, of course, though no one yet knows who'll be hit by arrows and who'll be hiding in the trees.'

Marta might have done well to know what sailors say is one of the most arduous tasks undertaken at sea: fishing for swordfish, a species that loves stormy weather and rough seas. To catch it, the crews head towards the storms, where they fish, cut off from the rest of the world, seven or eight hundred kilometres from the nearest coast: where the swell is violent and the storms pitilessly batter the ships, where winds as high as seventy knots threaten to tear the rigging apart and snap the masts. The fishermen generally have only two options – to prevail over the seas and fill their holds, or to sink without a trace.

The trouble was that Marta knew nothing of this, she had never even heard about fishing for swordfish. It was strange, then, that she so resembled those fishermen, that in many ways she was exactly like them. No one could stop her, no risk could daunt her, nothing would come between her and what she wanted. At eighteen, you already know that the opposite of winning is losing – but you don't yet know that you're not invincible.

She stood up and put on her raincoat. A glance at her watch told her that by now Lucas would not be coming to fetch her. Yet as she made her way out past two dozen young people hunched over typewriters – past that chaos of different styles: hesitant, alert, distracted, smiling, sad, despairing – she felt full of optimism, almost happy.

At the entrance, the director of the college said she had something to tell her, but Marta replied that she was in a hurry, on her way to visit her brother in hospital, and that the matter would have to wait until the following week. She left the premises, and walked in the rain, noting the complex beauty of the buildings, how the illuminated windows formed mysterious geometric patterns in the facades.

'You know what I've decided?' she would say to Lucas in two days' time, in one of the rooms of that house in the woods. 'That I should smash your face in. But don't worry – I'll still give you another chance.' No. I won't talk about other chances – that sounds too proud. 'You know what? I should smash your face in. But you're in luck – I've changed my mind, and now comes the fun part.' No. It sounds better without the 'you're in luck' part. 'You know what I've decided? I think I may well smash your face in. It wouldn't be a great loss: it's cute, but there are plenty more where you came from.' No, that's going too far. Don't force yourself into a corner you can't get out of. 'You know what I think? . . .'

Marta headed home in the dark, passing banks and pharmacies, supermarkets and shoe shops. The occasional passer-by gave her a brief look, noting her long strides, the way she walked, umbrellaless, head erect, face to the wind, briskly swinging her arms like someone on a mission.

When they return to dry land, when they leave their ships full of swordfish and bad dreams, the fishermen go to squalid hotels and sleep with sick women, or walk along the quays, where they eat dubious seafood and drink cheap liquor, and if anyone asks, they reply:

'Don't worry. Everything's fine. There's nothing can hurt you after you've been dead.'

IV

On turning her head for a moment she noticed a small crack – a fissure descending in a zigzag from the ceiling to almost halfway down the wall. It reminded her of the lightning that had struck Maceo, and for a while she stared at the flaking paintwork, so like the skin of a reptile, perhaps a lizard or a salamander, before she arched her back and gripped the edges of the mattress; closing her eyes and noting how because she was lying on her back, her tears, instead of running down her cheeks to her lips, ran backwards towards her temples.

She felt awful, in an indeterminate state in which anger, dejection, frustration, and remorse all mingled chaotically, like the pungent confusion of smells in a grocery.

The tears stung and left a brief burning trail that seemed to cut into the skin as it dried. Naturally, to Ruth these seemed another version of the crack in the wall.

But before all this took place, she had spent nine or ten days looking after Maceo and had noticed a variety of symptoms that indicated something was wrong: he was now – whether listening to one of Truman's stories, watching television, or reading a comic – given to suddenly falling asleep without the slightest warning. She and Samuel would exchange grave looks and watch him breathing so slowly and deeply that it was as if he were far inside the body of the boy they saw stretched out on the carpet or slumped in one of the living-room armchairs. Five, ten, fifteen minutes would pass before one of them carried Maceo to bed, where they had noticed he often did not move a muscle until he woke the following morning. Every time they checked, he was lying in exactly the position in which they had left him.

'Now, I'm not saying it's possible or impossible,' said the specialist she had telephoned to talk about Maceo, 'but tell me what you mean by *in exactly the same position*. Because in my view, that's a useful term for describing a corpse – not someone who's still alive.'

'Immobile, is what I mean. *Im-mo-bile*. All the parts of the body – the head, the neck, the fingers of each hand, the legs . . .'

'Listen to me a moment: the human body is jointed. Our bone structure . . .'

'For God's sake! I'm not talking about bone structure.'

'Ah, that's where you're wrong – you and all the other non-doctors who attempt a diagnosis. It is always – and I mean *always* – a question of bone structure, because that's all there is: neuroanatomy, bone structure, red and white blood cells . . .'

Ruth thanked him and brusquely said goodbye, telling herself that though his reasoning was scientific and therefore unanswerable, he was obviously more interested in logic than in facts. What was certain, however, was that in the days that followed, after visits to other consulting rooms and phone conversations with different specialists, she had received more of the same and no real replies – only digressions and evasions.

The second matter was even more puzzling, and it was Marta who noticed it first. She had observed that when her brother went to fetch a book from the study or returned from Truman's bedroom to his own, he did so in a very peculiar way: he always took the longest route.

49

The apartment had the following layout: a small hallway, with the kitchen to the left and Samuel's study to the right; from there, the corridor branched into two lateral passageways, one leading past the main bathroom and Truman's chambers to the living room, the other to Marta's quarters and Ruth and Samuel's bedroom. *Truman's chambers* was what Truman had chosen to call the tiny room where he slept, and *Marta's quarters* was the title that Marta had chosen in mocking homage to her grandfather's so-called chambers.

A separate corridor led from the living room to Ruth and Samuel's bedroom, such that, not only was Maceo's room situated at the very centre of the apartment, it was also the only room without windows – the others all had windows or balconies – and was surrounded on all four sides by an irregular rectangular corridor. There were two ways to interpret this: Maceo's room was either the cosiest room in the apartment, or it was the loneliest; and thus Maceo's liking for that entrenched area could be seen as the mark of his independent nature or of his tendency towards self-isolation.

What Marta had noticed was that when Maceo left Truman's room, for example, to return to his own, rather than turning right and then left – as would have been expected: a stretch of thirteen or fourteen metres – he did the exact opposite. He followed the long corridor in the other direction, passing the bathroom, the study, the hallway, the kitchen, Marta's room, and his parents' room. Ruth and Samuel at first thought that Marta was joking, but they soon realised it was true.

'We should take him to see a psychologist,' Ruth said.

'Good idea! And why not cut out the middleman and send Maceo straight to a mental hospital?'

'I'm being serious, Samuel.'

'Then stop talking nonsense.'

'What are you frightened of? Let me guess . . . it wouldn't be the expense, would it?'

'What am I frightened of? Jesus Christ, Ruth! What the boy needs is understanding and a little more time to recover – not to be treated as if he's mentally unbalanced.'

'Look, the only one around here behaving like a . . . a lunatic, is you.'

The argument did its work – poisoning, corrupting, wreaking havoc; it found words with which to infect its own wounds, tools to deepen the mutual rancour and disdain. And when, half an hour later, they had at last turned to face their respective sides of the bed, each breathing regularly to feign sleep, it went away, leaving them in the state it always did – full of hatred, but also remorse. How had they ever reached that point? Where did they find all that evil? And why did they allow it to overcome them?

Ruth knew the exact word which would explain it all, and that word was *respect*. She and Samuel had lost respect for each other long ago, and to such an extent that the sum of all the wrongs done and received had transformed them both, gradually reducing their life together to a dismal combat of low blows and vicious insults; to the worst kind of fighting, because whatever happened, no matter how disproportionate the hurt caused or suffered, neither she nor Samuel knew how to win nor how to surrender. At times, as happened on the evening Samuel had suggested Marta attend lessons at the secretarial college, Ruth's bitterness led her to see themselves as such ridiculous characters that she even began to wonder if she wasn't losing her mind. While Samuel explained to his daughter the usefulness of such skills, how one day they might be of benefit, Ruth found herself growing angrier and angrier, hating every sentence he uttered, every observation he made: when Samuel tried to be insightful, she thought him absurd; when he felt himself to be convincing, she found him grotesque. She sat there for several minutes, loathing the reasonableness in his voice, the way he chewed his food, his yellow pyjamas; substituting *mediocre* for *far-sighted*, *pathetic* for *intelligent* and *unhealthy* for *subtle*. Then, prompted by ill humour or perhaps merely tiredness, she began to wonder what her father might have said had he been there, sitting with them at the table, his hands placed decorously on either side of his plate, exuding an air of somewhat old-fashioned rectitude. She imagined him leaning towards her or her mother, as he often did at business functions or on family occasions when a speaker or guest said something not to his liking, and whispering in her ear: 'Hark at Mister High-and-Mighty!' Or better still: 'Never heard such twaddle!' Ruth began to smile, while in the background she heard snippets of her daughter's defence – *orbicular . . . deltoid . . . sternomastoid* – and Samuel looked at her in complete astonishment, or to be more exact, bewilderment, as he said to Marta:

'Fine. I admit that's the main part, the most important thing. But it's not everything.'

'Christ!' exclaimed her father, in her mind. 'Just listen to this joker!'

Ruth let out a sudden laugh. She left the table with the excuse of taking some cups to the dishwasher, briefly intercepting Samuel's angry gaze as she hurried away, and trembling with laughter when she heard him say:

'A little humility, Marta. That's all I'm asking of you. Don't lose sight of your ambitions, but learn to be a little more humble.'

52

Five minutes later, when he came into the kitchen to demand an explanation, his fists clenched, his mind full of *what's the matter with you, this is outrageous, I'm starting to get tired of your stupid ways*, Samuel found Ruth leaning against the refrigerator, her arms clutching her sides, as she cried so hard with laughter that her knees buckled and she could barely stand.

'Bloody hell,' he shouted, before slamming the door loudly behind him.

'Good riddance!' shouted Ruth's father in reply, from beyond the grave. 'You idiot!'

The upshot of the argument was that Ruth and Samuel spent a week hardly speaking, which brought them a period of tension, but also one of calm, for on these fairly frequent occasions when neither wanted to make up and each tried to avoid the other, they both had time to ask themselves questions and to draw their own conclusions. By the end of the week, Ruth had reached the conclusion that she was going to leave Samuel, and her question was: how had it come to that?

In the course of this self-imposed quarantine she had thought of many answers, though all seemed false or partial. Yet one thing was indisputably true: Samuel had changed. What she had yet to resolve was, when, why, and whose fault it had been. She pictured him once more during his university days: young, talented, powerful, full of ideas. She remembered the meeting after which he had been elected to the student executive committee and how in the weeks that followed she contrived to approach him, how she began attending more or less secret meetings at the Faculty of Arts, or in certain cafés and cinemas, where a group of them – considered revolutionaries, conspirators, Reds, or subversives, depending on who you believed – met to discuss plans and strategies.

In the midst of all those young men and women who talked politics with constant references to Mao and Engels; who boasted of having been arrested or beaten up by the police at rallies in support of everything from freedom of the press to the raising of miners' wages; who used words like *utopia*, *dialectic*, and *empirical*; who wore corduroy jackets and dark roll-neck jumpers, denim skirts or dresses with psychedelic motifs – among all those well-meaning idealists and power-seeking egotists, Ruth saw right from the start that Samuel stood out. He stood out precisely because he was the opposite of those around him – he was sensible and he was cautious. While others raised their voices, interrupting one another in an effort to impose their opinions, Samuel remained silent, on the margin of all commotion. When the arguments grew heated – *it's time to throw rocks . . . to split . . . to smash* – he always found a maxim with which to calm the waters: 'If we behave like animals, how can they treat us like people?'; 'Violence never helps, it only ever makes you guilty'; 'In this business, sooner or later it's the side that keeps taking the punches that wins.' So rapid was the rise in his prestige that he had soon reached the stage where he could afford to expend less and less effort while expecting greater and greater results, for people had started to multiply everything he did by two: if someone said at twelve o'clock that Samuel had had a ten-minute dip in the pool, by five o'clock someone else would be saying Samuel had just swum the English Channel. 'Heard what the guy shouted at the meeting?' they would say. Or 'Guess what he told the Dean!'

At this point everything around him seemed to change, adapting to Samuel in such a way that those close to him became his disciples or loyal supporters, and his enemies became subdued rivals who temporarily stopped trying to defeat him and looked instead for a place to hide – all of which meant that Samuel was becoming powerful. She wondered if he realised this. Did he know that power was not measured in the number of those who follow but in the number of those who flee?

Those were the days when, as she walked theatrically at his side through the university campus or as they left a crowded student bar amid jealous murmurs and admiring looks, Ruth felt that she was at the centre of something – that the world around her was no more than the area around the bull's-eye. She had so much faith in all of this, she felt so anchored to Samuel and so sure of her place in her new, impregnable existence, that had anyone asked about her own future, she would have told them it was written in the palm of Samuel's hand.

How had the two of them become a couple? She remembered that it had not been difficult, and that to ensure Samuel came running towards her all she did was place herself within reach. Her method of seduction had been straightforward, coming with the quiet confidence inspired by self-appraisal: she could offer a pure heart and an agile mind, on the inside; high cheekbones, feline eyes, firm heavy breasts and long legs, on the outside. So that none of this would pass unnoticed, Ruth spent the first three hours of her first date with Samuel talking about the films of François Truffaut; by the time the fourth hour began late afternoon had turned to night, and they had left the wall mirrors and marble-and-gilt columns of the Café Comercial for the underground dining room of a small restaurant, where she very slowly and strategically unbuttoned her coat to reveal her flawless charms. She caught

Samuel's stare, the way his glance seemed to chance time and again on her long legs, beautifully sheathed in transparent nylon tights, or on her round breasts moving braless and free under the close-fitting T-shirt, and for a moment she thought she could read his mind: he was removing her clothes, taking his time as he stripped her, as he kissed her, licked her, caressed her; now, they were in the back of a taxi; next, he had his arms around her, in the shower of a room in a cheap hotel.

'Yes . . . that is what . . .' he was saying, '. . . well, ehm, the basic idea behind *The 400 Blows* is . . .'

'Good gracious, Samuel, you look like a hungry cat staring at a goldfish bowl,' Ruth interrupted.

She still remembered the maroon blush that rose to his face, his expression – that of a child caught rummaging in a handbag – the way he pulled his hand from the table as if dropping a gun, only to replace it a moment later, palm up, whereupon Ruth had placed hers on his. They had each lowered their gaze. He was wearing Gorila shoes. She wore black boots. The tablecloth had a red-and-white check pattern. A vase of honeysuckle stood on every table. When they looked back up into each other's eyes, they discovered eternal, indestructible love.

What had caused the fire they felt for each other to go out? How had life contrived to douse them down; to set traps, to open divides? Each question seemed to lead Ruth further from an answer.

She still felt ill, and dizzy, and took firmer hold of the edges of the mattress. She recalled how swiftly Samuel had fallen, how, after the initial upsurge, his influence had progressively receded, just as a wave turns to foam, then wet sand, then leaves behind an empty beach. She remembered their honeymoon in New York, the suspicions that first started on that trip. How did she know, as they walked with their arms around each other in Central Park or over Brooklyn Bridge? In what tiny details about the young man with the devastating gaze and triumphant ideas could she already discern the mediocre, hunched figure he would become? What suddenly allowed her to foresee the lifeless, obedient look in his eyes that he had now, the look of a guy who could always do with a new pair of shoes.

She would almost certainly think about all that again this evening, when she arrived home. And about the other man, a colleague called Ramón who, two months earlier, had begun making lewd, unambiguous advances. She remembered the way he kept pestering her, day after day, and how she always avoided him. Until today. Until this afternoon when, for no precise reason, she had come with him to a room in a shabby hotel, to the bed on which she now lay, her skirt bunched around her waist, her shirt unbuttoned, as she stared at a crack in the wall, her eyes filling with tears.

Ruth let go of the mattress and caressed the back of the man she found so revolting, while he puffed and panted and whispered in her ear:

'Damn, you're so hot! D'you like it when I talk dirty? Eh, bitch? You know you've got great tits . . . You know that, don't you, Ruthie? You love it when I tell you, eh?'

And she answered:

'Mmh. I love it. Don't stop. Keep talking. Tell me I'm a bitch, a dirty whore.'

V

'My father once told me that if you spent a whole day staring at a sand clock you would lose your mind.'

'And is that true?'

'Yes. I wasn't sure before, but now I think he was right.'

'Seriously?' Maceo gazed at Truman to see if he was joking.

'Well, maybe not strictly speaking; but that's how things seem when you're eighty.'

'Seventy-nine.'

'Seventy-nine, eighty . . . What difference does it make? The point is it's an age when all your thoughts start with the words *in the past*. You know what they say though: no use crying over spilt milk.'

'Is that bad?'

'It's hard, that's what it is – hard. You're still too young to know this, but there are many things in this world that can't be explained with terms like *good* and *bad*.'

'So, why are you . . . are you always saying memories are fine things?'

'They are. Memories are fine things which were yours once, but not any more.'

'Like Cecilia?'

'Like Cecilia, like everything else. You know what is the best feeling you can have in life? It's the feeling you're about to start something. The feeling that every step you take will be a step forwards.'

'And now you don't think . . .'

'I'm not sure. I have a lot to be thankful for: you, Marta, Samuel. But I'd like to . . . It's hard to explain. Sometimes I think of how it all went so quickly, how I never had a chance to find out what was important and what wasn't.'

'You don't know?'

'I do now. Not that it matters – now it's already too late. You find out when it's already gone. Do you understand? When it's already beyond your reach. It's a pity that it has to be like that, but it's not until you lose something that you realise what you had.'

Maceo did not understand. He was even at a loss to explain the presence there in front of him of that other person his grandfather turned into every so often, on certain occasions, for the most part brief, when he became a sad, resigned old man, the opposite of his usual self. Where did this second Truman come from? How did he appear, as though from inside Truman – suddenly, like someone stepping out from behind a statue, with that tortured look on his face, the look of a soldier trudging in line with other prisoners?

They were standing by the window in the living room, each with a pair of binoculars hung around his neck, waiting for the time when they would be able to see the comet. The newspapers predicted that it would be visible between midnight and 3 a.m., so they still had a long wait ahead of them.

Outside, the storm had died down, leaving a thick fog through which the buildings seemed like the remains of a burnt city, houses in the aftermath of a bombardment.

'It's so illogical,' Truman added, 'that things – the things you do, that is – can, in a sense, be seen clearly only from a distance. Do you follow me?'

'No.'

59

'When they're happening, when they're still with you, you think about them in a certain way, but afterwards everything about them seems different. Who knows . . .? Shortly before he died, my father told me that the best years of his marriage had been during the worst years of his life. This was after the war, after having lost everything, when he and my mother were starting again from scratch, singled out by Franco's regime as undesirables.'

'But wasn't he a stationmaster?'

'Yes, in a village near Seville. As a boy, I used to spend my days hopping on and off the trains. My favourite game was to go from one stop to the next and then back home. I loved walking through the carriages, looking at all the passengers, talking with the ticket inspectors, seeing the rails from the driver's compartment – especially on hot summer days, when they shone like a ray of lightning across the landscape. Mind you, some of those very same kind men, who let me wear their caps or punch the passengers' tickets, were part of the squad that came to murder my father. That tells you all you need to know about what war is.'

'But they didn't kill him.'

'No. Luckily they didn't have time to.'

'He escaped?'

'Some Falangist friends got him out.'

'Were the Falangists good or bad?'

'Let's just say they were on the side of the bad guys, but that they weren't the worst.'

'What happened after that?'

'They had put him onto a lorry and were taking him off to the meadow, where they were going to shoot him, up against the wall of the football ground. My mother called these people she knew, and they immediately jumped into a car and raced off in pursuit.'

'And they saved him.'

'Yes. But it made him realise the danger we were in. And so he decided our lives had to change: the two of them went back to La Coruña, which is where my mother was born, and they packed me off to Central America. It turned me into a globetrotter and my parents into a couple of poor wretches.'

'Couldn't he get another job there with the railway company?'

'You must be joking! That was out of the question.'

'But he was a stationmaster.'

'He was a Republican. And in the Spain of 1939 that meant you were a nobody.'

'So no one wanted to give him a job.'

'They lived in the attic of a house belonging to relatives of my mother's. And guess where they got the money they were sending to me in Costa Rica?'

'No idea.'

'They were stealing wolfram and selling it to the Germans. Can you believe that? My father, of all people, trading with the Nazis!'

'What's wolfram?'

'It's a mineral. Also known as tungsten. Its resistance to heat is so great' – his voice suddenly took on the professorial tone he often adopted when speaking to Maceo – 'that it melts only at over 3,000 degrees. Just to give you an idea, it's what they use to make the filaments in light bulbs.'

'3,000 degrees!'

'That's why they give off light: at very high temperatures the filaments can remain incandescent without ever catching fire. Tungsten is as hard as platinum, but much cheaper.'

'Wow . . .!' Maceo was always surprised at the extent of

Truman's knowledge; and in his mind some of those words he liked so much began to gleam: magnesium, iridium, nickel, titanium, mercury, tin – all names that featured as part of the science course that he was taking in the laboratory at school. On many afternoons, the two of them would sit down together to revise the table of symbols for minerals.

'Sulphur?' Truman would ask, book in hand; and Maceo would reply:

'*S*.'

'OK. Gold?'

'*Au*.'

'Iron?'

'*Fe*.'

'Correct. Uranium?'

'*Ur*. No! Wait! . . . *U*, just *U*. That's right, isn't it?'

'Yes. Let's see now . . . Chromium?'

'*Cr*.'

'Very good. Tantalum?'

'*Ta*.'

'Silver?'

'*Ag*.'

They did the same for other subjects too, when Maceo had to learn the names of rivers, mountain ranges, or foreign capitals. Truman enjoyed studying with Maceo, and in among all the dates, facts, and figures, it was not unusual for him to find a story to tell, a trail leading back to some point on the trajectory of his long life.

'As I was saying,' Truman went on, 'Hitler needed the tungsten to build his tanks and guns, and Galicia had tungsten. So the Germans would dock their cargo ships in the port of La Coruña and buy the mineral from anyone who had some to sell, in whatever quantity, no questions asked. Conditions at that time were dreadful, people were surviving, sometimes for months on end, on nothing more than corn or oat bread and a thin soup called "dog broth" which they made by boiling fish heads.'

'Ugh!'

'Yes, that's what you might think now. But remember what I told you before: the value of things varies, depending on what's happening to you. From one day to the next a gold bracelet will cost less than a chicken and having a mattress becomes more important than owning a Picasso. It all depends on how hungry you are, how tired you feel.'

'I see.'

'My father stayed first in Santa Comba, then he headed down towards Pontevedra, to Vila de Cruces. It was there, in a wood by the banks of the Deza, that dozens of men and women would go to dig for tungsten, using any tool they could lay their hands on. They dug at night, furtively, under cover of darkness and behind the backs of the Civil Guard, and in the morning they'd sell the tungsten there and then to the black marketeers.'

'Who were they? The ones who sold it on to the Germans?'

'That's right. They would then smuggle it across the border at Irún. There was a rumour that for months the British Navy kept a submarine stationed in the Vigo estuary, to see if Spain was supplying tungsten to the Third Reich; but either the British weren't very clever or else they turned a blind eye, because everyone except them knew all about the convoys of dozens of lorries that came and went; knew too that the merchandise eventually entered France via the Basque Country in motorboats, or more often than not, in special railway carriages or goods wagons hooked up to the trains coming in from Portugal.'

'Why didn't they take it in their own boats?'

'Because they'd have sunk! We're talking about thousands of tons. Bear in mind the tungsten was mixed with quartz and that most of the people illegally digging it, from mines or from seams they found in the woods, had no means of separating the two. So the tungsten was sold in the state it was found.'

'And that's how your father made some money?'

'Quite a lot more than *some*. You see, the Nazis paid about five hundred pesetas per sackful. If you were lucky and you weren't shot by the patrols, in a couple of nights you could dig up enough to get by for a month.'

'So your parents got rich?'

'Are you joking? No, far from it. For a start, they were sending most of that money out to me in Central America until I could get myself more or less settled, first in Panama, then in Mexico. And besides, they couldn't afford to give the slightest impression of wealth, since they weren't earning it by honest, or at any rate legal means. Anyway, when the Second World War ended, the business collapsed.'

'And your mother, what did she do?'

'Nothing! Just slowly went to pieces. She got a job as a cleaner in a school. Wiping desks, blackboards, scrubbing floors, cleaning windows. "The lovely Delia", they used to call her when she was young. Imagine her at nineteen or twenty, with her pale hands and ultramarine eyes, strolling by the beach, in a pink dress and sun hat.'

In Maceo's mind, a woman resembling her did indeed take a dozen or so steps along a narrow lamplit street. She was walking arm in arm with two other girls, and laughing. Delia turned towards him. She carried a small parasol over her shoulder, and wore red lipstick and a green ring. He wanted to run up to her, tell her what would happen to her in a few years' time. But just then, Truman said:

64

'And then picture her a little later, doing that job, condemned to work on her hands and knees, dressed like a servant.'

Maceo noticed the way Truman pronounced these words – *servant, hands and knees* – as if they were pieces of ice that he was chewing painfully between his back teeth.

'But your father told you he'd been happier than ever before, during that period.'

'That's true. I suppose the misfortune they had to share was so great that they had never felt as close as they did then. What the hell could they do? They were like a pair of dogs knocked into the same ditch by a passing truck.' On seeing the look of horror, or alarm, on Maceo's face, Truman decided to tone down what he had just said. 'I guess it's how two people who love each other would carry a very heavy object – each one struggling desperately to keep their own end up, trying to share the weight out fairly: seventy kilos for you, seventy for me.'

'I see.'

'At night they'd shut themselves away in their attic,' Truman said, getting up to turn on the radio, 'with only a small heater by their bed.'

'A gas heater?'

'No. I don't think so. It probably needed firewood.' Truman glanced round the room, perhaps in search of a way back, an exit through which to flee that rathole where his parents led such a miserable existence. 'Or coal. But let's hear the news now. OK with you? Still interested in that comet? I bet you are. After all . . . I mean, what with the lightning and . . . I don't know.' He gave Maceo a smile. 'It's as if somehow . . . well, somehow you were part of all that.'

They heard the sound of the front door closing. What seemed to Maceo like hesitant, unfamiliar steps approached along the corridor, and he saw his father pass on the way to the main bedroom. His father, too, seemed different, as though something about him were either lacking or superfluous, though Maceo could not have said which was the case.

He looked back at Truman again. Three or four thumps rose from the floor below: the butcher had a customer.

What could he see around him? Oddly proportioned rooms; floors of fresh cement; furniture sunk in murky water; objects that kept shifting – an alarm clock, a bedside lamp, a book – their outlines as hazy as the edges of burning wood.

Samuel closed his eyes. Opened them again, expecting everything to vanish. It did not; each object remained in place, giving off a ghostly glow that entered him like sunlight through the stained glass of a Byzantine church.

He lay back on the bed, but the whole room spun in his mind in a swirl of fragments, pieces from the world outside: a debris of chests of drawers, net curtains, radiators.

He sat up again.

He stared down at his hands. They looked small, as if they were those of a man seen at a distance, a man in another bed, three or four rooms away.

He vaguely recalled standing at the bar in the clinic, drinking four or five bottles of beer, then a couple of glasses of whisky; all the while feeling more and more fragile but less vulnerable too. He felt fine now – as though the whole thing had never happened. He knew this to be untrue, but also that he had no choice but to think so: it was either a lie or the abyss; and so he chose the long way round, as most of us almost always do; he did not want the truth, merely a little more time. Why? What for?

Several thoughts had lodged in his mind, where they floated, unchanging, in a kind of stagnant water: the girl he had followed after work a week before; the row he had had with Ruth; Maceo's stay in hospital and the strange consequences of the lightning strike. It had all come together in recent days and left him distraught, utterly confused. Wherever he was, whether at the office, at home, or walking in the street, he could never shake off the sense of being lost, oddly adrift, like the shattered statue whose pieces passers-by had taken home on the evening of the storm.

What was there to say about his marriage? That it was foundering, was plain to see; but on what rocks had it run aground? What iceberg had it struck? On a journey from where to where? Samuel took stock of all the things they had said to each other in the course of their arguments; he counted the fractures, the bruises, the wounds; he recognised that the effects of that never-ending struggle were devastating, that the increasing viciousness of their attacks had led each to hate the other deeply. Yet that was the strangest part of all, for hatred was supposed to be what set in when all else had disappeared, and his impression was that the opposite was currently the case: that love, desire, complicity, and the long list of other emotions Ruth and he had shared when they first became a couple, were all still there beneath that mud, alive amid the rubble. To Samuel they were merely something that Ruth and he had mislaid, which was still theirs; something still out there somewhere, just waiting for them to go and fetch it back. Seeing matters in that light did not make them any more bearable, though; it simply made failure all the more acute. Why did the two of them behave like that? What drove them to this form of suicide, to the sadistic pleasure of tearing each other apart? And why, if they were both mature adults who should have loved each other, did they insist on acting like those little children who sit down calmly on the kitchen floor, only to take their favourite toys painstakingly apart?

Samuel did not have the answers. All he knew was that if there were but two kinds of relationship in the world – those we wish were over and those we don't – his relationship with Ruth belonged unquestionably to the second category.

Well, then?

He felt ashamed to recall an absurd episode, brought about by a series of rows with Ruth. It came at a time when she was accusing him of treating her like a waitress, an ironing lady, a servant; this had so offended him that every evening, on getting home from the office, he had obstinately locked himself away in his study and refused to eat the supper Ruth prepared. Night after night, over the course of the next four or five days, Ruth had left the spurned dishes to accumulate on the table, perhaps – Samuel supposed – as proof of how stupid and immature he was. Every morning, on coming in to prepare his own breakfast, he had been greeted by the sight of an omelette, rice, fried chicken, a sole, pasta, half a dozen croquettes, all placed around a glass of water and some accusingly untouched cutlery, each dish covered in plastic film and looking about as appetising as the dangling corpse of a general hung by guerrilla forces.

What had been the point of it all? There had been no point, he was sure of that now, except to make everything worse; to spend the entire next day in a state of frustration, alone and getting more and more furious, blinded by hunger and rage, storing up so much hatred towards his wife that the further their battle receded into the past, the more his resentment grew, instead of melting away.

Samuel wanted to turn the clock back and conduct matters differently, starting from the day he first behaved in that absurd way: a Friday in July, three years before. Ruth knocked on his door and this time he went to open it. It was that easy – a simple matter of taking a dozen or so paces, turning a key, letting their lives start up again. Better still, he opened the door and said: 'Forgive me'. Nothing more.

But he had not done so. Neither on that occasion nor on those that followed. Instead he stayed right where he was, listening to the alarming sound of Ruth's knuckles against the wood, wishing with all his heart that he could behave otherwise. Why, then, had he persisted? Where did he find all that pride? How did he get to be so stupid, so conceited, or perhaps, so cowardly? Why had he never managed to understand that the only way two people ever go forward together is by each taking a few steps back?

Many of their plans had not come to fruition, that much was obvious; they had not always made the best choices when life forced them to decide between their dreams and their needs. Ruth, he felt certain, thought that she deserved more; perhaps twice as much as she had now. But what an uncomfortable feeling it was to look back and find that your plans from the past appear so remote, like the name of a country in which you have never set foot; they seem to resemble something which could hardly ever have been yours, which you regard with the same disbelief you experience at seeing the clothes you wore as a child, as you stand there in the attic or the cellar of your mother's house, clutching a cardboard box, telling yourself: it can't be, just look how small those gloves are, and that anorak, those little red shoes . . .

But in any case, what gave her the right to take on the role of victim? Who was it, over the past twenty years, that

70

had striven hardest to provide for the family? Of the two of them, who had always remained on dry land while the other went out and braved the waters? What could be more unfair than accusing him of having made no sacrifices for his family? How dare she criticise his job, the way he dressed, the home he had bought by dint of so much effort and self-denial? Why was it more demeaning to lag behind than not to take part in the race at all?

Samuel then realised that he was not merely asking himself these questions; he was also trying them out, getting them ready for his next row with Ruth. So he tried to put them out of his mind, and almost succeeded in doing so by concentrating on the pattern in the carpet – a series of brown, orange, and grey circles – which they had bought precisely *because* it was hideous and reminded them of 'a room in a no-star hotel'. That was how Ruth had put it.

'A no-star hotel?' Samuel repeated, with the same tone of voice and look of surprise of ten years earlier. 'What's so special about those hotels, except for the dirty sheets and decrepit bathrooms?'

'The sheets are dirtier – as are the affairs,' came Ruth's reply.

Samuel smiled and cast his gaze over the carpet, searching for a dark stain that had been there ever since the afternoon they made it, when the apartment was still unfurnished and Ruth had opened a bottle of cava.

'Come here,' she said from where she sat on the floor, her back against the wall, a cigarette in one hand. 'Let's have a toast to the ugliest carpet ever made.'

He stared across at her from the other side of the room. To him she seemed the sweetest woman on Earth, with her wavy hair and denim dress, as radiant and full of promise as a city seen from a plane at night.

'OK,' he replied, 'but I'm not a big fan of champagne.'

'Well, what a shame,' she said, lowering the straps of her dress and pouring a trickle over her breasts. 'I'm sure it's not that bad.'

Now, so many years later and having drifted so much further apart, Ruth had long since ceased to be that provocative girl who behaved at times as if she were not subject to the same rules as other people, Samuel found he still desired her almost as intensely as he had on that afternoon. It was a feeling he often wondered about, and one which was, it seemed, uncontaminated by their arguments, or one which had at least survived intact, like the still edible part of a rotting apple. He remembered the evening when he suggested to Marta that she enrol at the secretarial college, the way Ruth had laughed at him; and how, on entering the kitchen to demand an explanation and finding her roaring with laughter, her lips moist, her dress stained with oil or water, several undone buttons on her shirt revealing a plunging neckline, he had not wanted to insult her or hit her, he had wanted to make love to her, right there and then, up against the refrigerator, despite and on top of all that had happened.

Yet this was what often occurred: his confrontations with Ruth were not something he sought, but something he could not avoid – to such an extent that frequently, in the course of an argument, he felt strangely certain that the words he came out with were beyond his control, not of his prompting, like the twitches of someone sleeping.

'This has got to stop,' Samuel thought. 'I'll make sure it does. Not even . . . We can't be the people we've become, for God's sake!'

But then he remembered Ruth's indomitable nature once again; the scathing sarcasm she so often used to make him feel despised, insignificant; the way she would let her rancour grow until it became so intense it reversed the laws of perspective. And what was left behind, instead of becoming smaller or lessening in importance, loomed ever larger the more distant it became. Where did the woman get all her arrogance? Where did she get her sense of superiority? What was so good about her that she could assign him a subordinate role? Instead of blaming him, why didn't she blame herself for failing to reach the status she so felt she deserved?

Samuel continued mulling over these questions. Again he had that look about him of a man sitting in the dark, sharpening a knife. Suddenly he got up from the bed, took a few steps, glanced about him, made an abrupt gesture with his right hand: that's it, I've had enough. Then, lying down again, his eyes closed, he found his other hand clutching the keys that belonged to the second girl, the girl he had followed that afternoon, after work, to a patch of waste ground, where she had let them fall, perhaps on purpose, perhaps not, and run off.

In the distance, he could hear the faint sound of Truman and Maceo's voices:

'United Arab Emirates?'

'Abu Dhabi.'

'Uganda?'

'Kampala.'

'Egypt?'

'Cairo.'

There was no denying that what he had done worried him, but part of it also excited him: the girl's face turning to look back as she fled, the sound of her voice shouting 'Oh my God, no, oh my God', the sound of the keys striking the ground. Samuel gave a faint smile, then pressed his fingers to his temples to relieve an intense pounding – a deafening disproportionate throb, rather as if he were a monster with a single head and ten hearts. Then he glanced at his watch, wondering where Ruth could be, why she hadn't yet come home. 'These keys feel so strange,' he mused, 'it's as though I had hold of a dove, a small, angular skeleton, moving as though trying to escape, I can almost hear a heartbeat . . . squeeze, and it's just like crushing the tiny bones of a dove.'

After that he closed his eyes in an expression of surrender, the expression of a man letting himself go under, of a captain striking his ship's colours. 'Never again,' he muttered, though he would have been hard-pressed to define the part of all that had happened and all that he had thought, to which these words related.

'Somalia?'

'Mogadishu.'

'Congo?'

'Kinshasa.'

'Tanzania?'

'Dar es Salaam.'

CHAPTER THREE

I

Marta was travelling in a car and staring up at the sky, on the lookout for any clue or sign of the comet. Watching the sky from inside a moving car produces a peculiar sensation, especially on one of those clear, cloudless, seamless mornings: buildings, trees, all are on the move, flowing towards you then being left in your wake; the sky, though, remains unchanged, seemingly separate, its stillness unaffected by your speed. It stays true to itself, while down below, a square with people and shops becomes a wood, a railway station gives way to open fields.

If the comet really was going to be visible that evening, she could watch it at the party, she decided; she had a vision of herself and Lucas holding hands on the bank of a river, their faces tilted heavenward, music playing in the background. What would the song be? Something by Public Enemy? Massive Attack? Or perhaps something less recent, like The Grateful Dead? She shook her head, trying to put all this to one side and concentrate instead on the events that would unfold in an hour's time; imagining how she would win Lucas back, have him once more for herself. But had she ever really lost him, she wondered. When? And, more importantly, why? Marta appeared to absolve him of any guilt, as she tried to recall if in recent months she had done anything which could explain his desertion. She often wondered whether he had left her for good – and that fear became something very unsettling, something from which it was so hard to avert her gaze, as vague yet terrifying as the form of a corpse lying beneath a sheet.

'Remember the guess-the-car game we used to play? Remember the day I beat Marta 10–0? 10–0! That was such bad luck!'

This was said by Enara, one of the other two girls going to the party in the woods with Marta. Given that she is in no way one of this story's main characters, little attempt has been made to learn much about Enara; if we confine ourselves to what Marta thinks of her, however, then it has to be said that she is perhaps a somewhat ambiguous figure, someone hard to fathom, one of those harmless-looking people who always know just how to hurt you; who may seem meek and resigned, but who somehow manage to strike once, twice, a thousand times in a row, while you sit there wondering whether they can really be as stupid as they seem, or whether they are simply slyly evil. With these suspicions in mind, Marta had not known what to make of Enara's comment about her bad luck. She remembered that absurd game in which everyone had to pick a colour and then keep a score of all the cars of that colour that passed the window. Marta usually chose green and Enara yellow. It had been Enara who phoned on the day the lightning struck Maceo.

The third passenger in the car was behind the wheel; she was called Iraide, and she usually chose red. She was also Enara's sister, though the complete opposite of her. Her role in life was to pretend to be self-confident and unscrupulous, to pass herself off as superficial and frivolous and thereby catch out the unwary with sallies of a devastatingly savage wit, trained to cut the pretentious down to size and to give the conceited something to remember until their dying day. Relations between her and Marta were far from easy, for they were based on a contradictory mix of affinities and disparities, a shared history of complicity and tacit understanding – clear testimony to a trustworthy, intransigent nature in which loyalty was guaranteed and the slightest show of emotion forbidden. Iraide was always ready to take a stand on some point that was halfway between *all* and *nothing, me* and *you*; and of all the words in the dictionary, the word that best described her general behaviour was *unpredictable*. As Marta liked to put it, had Enara been the Gobi Desert, Iraide would have been a deep-sea diver. Marta, it seemed, knew that one girl was much quicker than the other, but not that they were both of equal strength.

'10–0?' Iraide said. 'If this pen-pusher beat you 10–0 at anything, get out of the car.'

Marta was still gazing intently at the sky, at the darkness gathering in the pines as they drove further up into the mountains. For several seconds she fantasised an avalanche: she and Iraide were in a ski lift, from where they witnessed a great wash of snow come crashing down over the trees, over the slopes busy with skiers, over the buildings.

'I don't think that's true,' she replied eventually, turning to look round at Enara. 'If she had ever really beaten anybody 10–0, she wouldn't be smiling like that after someone called her a pen-pusher.'

'Touché!' Iraide yelled. 'Checkmate!'

But despite this, Enara continued to smile. Then she said:

'Well, from what I've heard, Marta isn't unbeatable.'

'At what game?' Iraide asked.

'Well . . . it's not unknown for other people to win things off her.'

79

In the wake of the avalanche, Marta recalled, the Red Cross helicopters and army rescue teams had combed the area to the point of exhaustion, but by the time they found the body, Enara had been dead for two days.

'Things? . . . What kind of things?'

'Oh, you know . . .'

'Is that so?' Marta felt she had to cut in. 'I thought you were the one who knew something.'

'Yes, but I already told you about Luisa . . . and all the rest of it.'

'*And all the rest of it*? What the fuck does that mean? Luisa and Europe? Luisa and the Mediterranean?'

'Luisa and the Dalai Lama!' Iraide shouted, turning up the volume on the radio. 'Luisa and the Great Wall of China! Hey, listen, this is Dover! I love this band.'

Marta knew that they were only marking time and that Enara was not about to let go that easily. She felt helpless, trapped. Like a fugitive caught on a barbed-wire fence. 'Things that are yellow,' she thought to herself: 'dirty teeth, faded cotton underwear, the eyes of wolves.' Then she remembered something she had once learnt about deserts: deserts were either hot or cold. The Sahara, the Turkestan and the Gobi were hot deserts, as were the Arizona and the Kalahari. The polar deserts were in Greenland and the Antarctic.

'So,' Enara went on, 'what are you going to do about it?'

'Jump out of a moving car if you don't shut up.'

'But it seems like she and Lucas did go to that hotel.'

'Not true.'

'That's what people are saying.'

'What people? Oh come on, Enara, don't give me that! People say all kinds of rubbish. Some people think the anvil is a bone in the nose. Some people think the Ganges flows through Warsaw.' Her rapidly spreading anguish gave the word 'Warsaw' an odd nuance. She tried to smile, to calm herself down. But, from the back seat, Enara wanted to go on twisting the knife.

'I spoke to Luisa in the changing rooms yesterday. She went to Paris once, you know. She says . . . about going to hotels, I mean . . . that the French do it all the time. So it's not as if there's anything unusual about students doing it.'

'Listen, darling,' Iraide cut in, 'what Luisa knows about Paris could fit into the back pocket of a tracksuit.'

'Yeah, well . . . you're funny today. But this time I think she's . . .'

'Why don't you shut up.'

'. . . *this time* I think Luisa's . . .'

'Shut the fuck up! OK? Just shut it! I couldn't care less about *this time* or any other time.'

'But I was only . . .'

'. . . Up yours, Enara! What you need is to find yourself a guy at the party, take him behind a tree, and suck him till his eyes pop. Though you're probably too stupid to know how.'

'What's that supposed to mean? What are you trying to . . .'

'Being a virgin is driving you mad. If someone doesn't give you one soon . . .'

'Iraide!'

'If someone doesn't give you one soon, we'll have to get you a straitjacket.'

'Fugh . . .'

'Fuck you. Repeat after me: *Fuck you*. Jesus Christ! You can't even pronounce the word properly.'

Then Iraide turned the music up so high that the car's bodywork began to pulse: end of story, enough said.

81

Sitting stiffly beside her, Marta was less aware of that deafening buzz than of the skilful way in which Enara had known how to rekindle her fears, to the point where they now turned her mind into a dark place, a city that lived in fear, a city where escaped tigers roamed the empty streets. What precisely did she feel in that moment? Anxiety? Indecision? Panic? It was hard to say for certain – she herself did not know. What lay beyond doubt, however, was this: if in a person's life there exists a seminal mistake – a pivot or axis around which all their misery will never cease to spin – Marta reached that point exactly two minutes later, when she promised herself that Lucas would be hers for ever, at whatever cost. This was no figure of speech, these were the exact words she used: 'For ever. At whatever cost.'

Desert lands hold nothing, no help, no hope; only nights without end, blazing days. Those who cross them feel so alone that on occasion they prefer to give up and die rather than go on advancing in search of a How, a Why, a How Much Further. Hot deserts. Cold deserts. How terrible it must be to die in the midst of nothing, with the xerophilous plants and the hyenas and the scorpions.

Enemies never disappear, they merely retreat. This is what Ruth learnt at Samuel's side. Enemies retreat to a point where they are out of sight, to a place where you forget they exist. There they become fanatical and pitiless, seek reasons for each of their wounds, and when they have found them, choose one of their number to go back and destroy you.

Samuel never admitted that this was what happened to him, that this could have been the cause of his fall from on high, back in his days as a student. And yet, although whenever the subject came up in conversation he neither argued it one way or the other nor said it in so many words – instead affecting the weariness or disinterest of someone who has long since chosen to rule himself out of the struggle – Ruth sensed that the resentment and frustration had never left him. Why had he let others snatch away what had once been his? It was obvious, in her view, that Samuel had been naïve, or at the very least, had proved himself to be a poor strategist who never reckoned with the rage of those he left behind, the fury all losers can muster; who never realised that he was at war and that in a war, as she once heard him say to her father, the victorious army's strength is measured by the number of the vanquished army's dead. Ruth clearly remembered his tactic of being magnanimous towards his rivals; how, for example, after a meeting or assembly at which he had publicly ridiculed another boy's views, Samuel would always attempt to ingratiate himself in private – perhaps by prompting a chance meeting in the cafeteria or the corridors of the faculty, whereupon he would justify himself, offer to help resurrect what he himself had knocked down. Ruth had often mentioned this to him, and on more than one occasion she had warned him of the dangers of an attitude that was so indiscriminately conciliatory; but Samuel as he was then – so immune to doubt, so sure of himself – never heeded advice, never hesitated.

'It's a question of balance,' he would reply. 'You see, if you stoke the boiler with too much coal, the flames go out, and instead of going faster, the ship stops moving.'

'The ship? I'm talking . . . How did a ship get into the conversation? Look,' Ruth had laughed but now she was serious again, 'I don't really think you can ever be friends with someone you've just defeated. It's not natural. It may not even be healthy. You might perhaps also . . .'

'Defeated?' Samuel would have taken hold of her arm or started to kiss her neck. 'Where did you get that idea? I don't want to defeat them, I want to convince them.'

'But did you see the way he was looking at you? He didn't want to be convinced; he wanted to murder you.'

'Don't worry about him. His ambitions are harmless. Couldn't you tell? Harmless and of the worst kind: he doesn't know what he wants, and even if he did, he wouldn't know how to achieve it.'

In time, and with the disappointments that were to come, they would both grow to realise that Samuel's brilliance was not enough, that his benevolent ways represented a form of suicide, and also that his stature as a leader was less than they had expected. Hence when failure, then the need for compromise, and then finally ostracism became a part of their life, they felt a devastating sense of shock and helplessness; they experienced the kind of humiliation people feel when they go from believing themselves invulnerable to finding themselves defeated.

Ruth was pondering all this on her journey home across the city centre, in the taxi she had taken after leaving the office; though by turns, she also thought back to the night of the comet and the afternoon she had slept with Ramón almost without knowing why, feeling an obscure need to do so, an uncontrollable urge which in any case was not so much directed at Ramón, as away from Samuel. Was that what it was, then? Revenge? An act of spite? Of madness? The thought of her own infidelity made her feel corrupt; she felt no better, just dirtier, more contaminated, as if her lover had infected her with a disease. And yet after the first meeting there had been two more that week, one in the same sordid hotel as on the first occasion and another – unprecedented for her – in the toilet of a bar, as dusk fell on a day that had begun to go wrong over breakfast as a result of a domestic quarrel resumed seven hours later via the telephone, something about some pieces of meat that had gone off and which Samuel had found that morning at the back of the refrigerator; an argument that moved on to other matters and found paths to deeper issues, in that way resentment has of connecting some subjects to certain others, of linking up one wound with several more.

'All I know is that until we're millionaires we can't afford to throw food in the bin. And even if we were – have you watched television or opened a newspaper recently? People are starving – in Africa, in South America, in India, and in countries . . .'

'Oh, please! You couldn't care less about other people. It's not wasting meat that bothers you, it's wasting money.'

'Sure it is! It's always the same old story with you spendthrifts: other people are misers. Go on, deny it.

85

Misers and demagogues. Which gives you the perfect excuse for your selfishness and lack of solidarity. Does the opposite of waste always have to be avarice?'

'Oh, ha, ha. Mister Let's-Save-the-World and his heart of gold.'

'Laugh as much as you like. You have no respect for anything – which makes you not only stupid, but despicable too.'

'Despicable is exactly what you are: Sophisticated Insults plc, that's your usual style.'

'I'm not insulting you, I'm simply . . .'

'Don't worry – water off a duck's back. The sad thing is, you're not even lying to yourself: you wouldn't know the first thing about generosity. You're no altruist, you're just plain greedy; you're far too much of an egoist ever to be charitable.'

'Egoist! Coming from you! That really is a joke. You're such a narcissist that . . . Have you ever thought about anything other than how clever you are, how gorgeous you are?'

'Yes, I can't stop thinking about . . .' Ruth's voice seemed to falter: 'how unlucky I am that . . . but you're so busy feeling sorry for yourself you don't . . . that it's . . .'

'No! That's where you're wrong. The people I feel sorry for are us; and for what you've done to our life.'

'Look, Samuel, it's not me who's to blame – it's you. And if you call this a life, then my name's Winston Churchill.' In less than a second, sarcasm had restored her voice to normal.

'Me? How? Because of my work? Because of all the efforts I've made to keep our heads above water?'

'Because of your meanness, because of your need to control absolutely everything, because of your . . . your . . .'

'What? Because of my what?' He tried to guess the word she wasn't saying – mediocrity, madness, gullibility? – but he too lacked the courage to say it . . . 'All I want is for things in our home to run smoothly. All I want, Ruth, is to find a way back.'

'Where to? Where from?'

'Something that relates to the two of us. Something with which to . . .'

'The two of us? You and I stopped being *the two of us* a long time ago.'

Samuel's eyes flashed with anger. He looked across to the other side of the kitchen and Ruth followed his gaze. On top of the dishwasher lay a knife.

'You're nobody any more, Ruth. You're nobody because you've given up. You used to be gentle, understanding. You used to be cheerful . . .' He got up to leave the room. 'What happened to you? I don't think you know. What's made you so malicious, so vile?'

Now, in the taxi taking her home a few days later, Ruth returned for another morning in that kitchen, and replaced everything she had previously said with phrases that were less awful, more fitting; she calmly conducted matters along a different route: instead of a bare table, there were two cups of coffee; instead of trading insults, they spoke to each other in a civilised manner; and when she caught him staring at the knife, she didn't even feel afraid.

Things look better when seen from a distance, Ruth told herself; when there seemed to be no solution, they would then look so easy, so workable. But all that was sheer fantasy, lies. The truth consisted of callousness, of dirt, of stench; of the insults she traded with Samuel; of the incident in the bar where she had gone that afternoon with Ramón, of that disturbing scene she couldn't put out of her mind: he astride the toilet and she kneeling at his feet, as she felt, welling up inside her, the shame that had remained with her ever since, a shame that she could not get rid of, a portable pain accompanying her everywhere she went. From what hidden reserves had she drawn so much energy, the drive needed to sink so low? The answer was Samuel. The answer lay in that life Samuel was pushing her to accept, a life so dismal, so like the circus in Bilbao where the lion-tamer had abandoned one of his lions; so like that marginal world, home to a fake fakir, a frightened trapeze artist, and a poor devil whose human-cannonball costume had shrunk.

'Like all liars you're never guilty, are you?' Samuel said to her, from another day, another argument.

'At least I'm not a con man. At least I don't pretend to be something I'm not. You, though, you're a real fraud, you're cynicism personified . . . What happened to me?' she went on, though she was now back in the kitchen on the morning they had started arguing about the meat. 'Who wants to know? The great Samuel? The man who aimed so high? Just take a look at yourself now – with your disgusting stripy pyjamas and your thermal vests. And don't look round for a gun – there's nothing to shoot at.'

The taxi driver was watching her in the rear-view mirror. Had she been talking aloud? She needed to calm down. She lit a cigarette. Her thoughts returned to that first morning at the university, to that lecture hall where the students were holding their meeting and the boy in the red shirt had just stepped onto the platform, and she changed all this too: instead of feeling drawn to Samuel, she carried on with her self-portrait, making a determined effort, until her features gradually emerged – the slightly feline eyes, the straight nose, the cheekbones. 'It's wonderful to be there,' she thought, 'and to have this second chance; because that way, everything's going to be different, none of this ever happened.'

Then she thought about the night of the comet, and remembered that this had been the day when she had first planned how she was going to kill Samuel.

III

'You realise it when someone who truly matters to you dies and you discover that the hole this person leaves behind will be there for ever, that you won't be able to fill it in again because nothing will ever be big enough. That's when you learn that time does not pass, time empties. Does that make sense to you? What I mean is that life is not about what you win, but about what disappears, and that this is something you can't even begin to imagine when you're young. Later on you do – everyone does – but not at first. At first you're full of optimism, carefree, you think everything will always be there no matter what you do . . . It's like seeing an abyss open up in front of you. You think to yourself, if I didn't know about something as big as this, what else don't I know about?'

Truman was digressing in this way in order to help Maceo understand what he felt when he learnt that his mother – the lovely Delia – had died.

'So you got the letter in Mexico?'

'That's right.'

'Why did you leave Costa Rica?'

'Well, before that I'd been in Panama.'

'OK, but why did you leave Costa Rica?'

They were talking alone in Truman's room, though the conversation itself had started over dinner, amid an atmosphere of tension, with Marta and Ruth taking refuge behind a wall of silence, and Samuel, very pale, with that haggard, convalescent look he had of late, continually bringing a hand up to his stomach and giving in to violent fits of coughing.

'In San José I had met some Spaniards who owned a furniture shop. Cecilia's father introduced me, and they offered me a job.' As Truman said this, the boy realised that he only ever mentioned Cecilia when they were alone, never in front of Samuel. 'I was lucky they turned up when they did, because by then I was penniless.'

'Your parents had stopped sending you money?'

'The Second World War was over and so was the trade in tungsten. I had been in Costa Rica for six years. My mother was suffering from asthma and had to stop working. For a period my father worked on a trawler, after which he managed to get a job on a stall in the fish market, though what he earned was barely enough to live on. You know what my mother found hardest of all? The smell of fish; my mother had always hated fish, she said she couldn't stop looking at the eyes. I saw my parents have the same conversation a thousand times, before the war, as we walked down from the railway station in Seville on the way to eat in one of the city's restaurants. "What eyes do you mean, Delia?" my father would say to her. "No one is asking you to eat the eyes." And she'd reply: "You know exactly the ones I mean – all of the ones on the market stalls: hake eyes, tuna eyes, sardine eyes. Those horrible things, lying there in those crates of ice, staring out at you, with those little circles and their . . . their *dampness* . . . that stud of death at their centre. Why don't they cut the heads off?" Whereupon my father would point at the half-eaten steak or piece of roast chicken on her plate: "But cows also have eyes. And so too do chickens." She'd start to smile, and blush; my God, it's as if she were here in front of me right now, just sitting there, looking down at the tablecloth, a fork in one hand, a gold medallion of the Carmelite Virgin round her neck – because she was Catholic, you see, a Republican but also a Catholic: she always said you had to believe in both freedom and God, and that Jesus was a revolutionary, a friend of the people. It's funny now to think how my father used to make fun of her and her habit of going to mass on Sundays; that every week, just as she was about to leave for church, he'd tease her by saying "Where's my pious little darling off to this time, pray tell?" Because in the end it was precisely her churchgoing that saved his life, as many kept reminding him afterwards: "Eh, you old fool, what with all the mistakes you've made, you're lucky Delia's a saint, otherwise . . . "'

'Is that where she met the Falangists, in church?'

'Yes. Them and all the others who were always there – the families of landowners, cattle ranchers.'

'And so she hated the smell of fish?' Maceo glanced at the chair on which lay the two pairs of binoculars he and Truman had used to watch the comet.

'She loathed the smell of the clothes he wore at work in the market; but not because of how he smelt, but because, she said, when she washed them the smell rubbed off on her hands and it didn't go away, no matter how much soap she used. "You know, if I close my eyes I can still smell that perfume you used to like," my father told me she said to him, one night in that borrowed attic in La Coruña, as they sat by the heater, in darkness but for an oil lamp. "The one I'd put on to go to parties." And my father replied: "The one we thought was a mixture of mint and lilac." And she said: "I only wish that was the fragrance you were coming home to these days!" Then he took hold of her hand, which by now would have lost all of the pearly grace it had possessed in her youth and was reddish and rough instead, and said: "Do you think I care what you smell of – all I care about is you." And she'd reply: "Strange though, isn't it, how there are some smells you never forget, how you can even feel a longing for a smell."'

'Tell me about what happened in Panama,' interrupted Maceo, in whom this kind of story produced a sense of unease and brought to mind ill-defined, sinister thoughts somehow relevant to him. Ill-defined and sinister thoughts of something that was heading his way.

Truman looked at him for a moment, as if weighing up which of all the things he could say next was the most appropriate. Then he continued his story:

'My mother played a role in that too, because most of the Spaniards in exile in Panama were from Galicia; so when Cecilia's father told them that Delia came from La Coruña . . . well, you know what people are like when it comes to that kind of thing: they made a special effort to help me. Life in Spain was hard. I had to accept whatever I was offered.'

'You didn't want to leave?'

'Of course not! Why would I want to leave, if the work was in Panama and Cecilia was in Costa Rica?'

'But her father . . .'

'Her father got me a job as far away as he could, in a place where I couldn't lay a finger on his daughter.'

'He didn't like you, then?'

'Who knows. I don't think he ever stopped to give it much thought. He simply didn't like what I was.'

'What you were?'

'A good-for-nothing. You know what kind of a person that is? The kind who has no money and no means of earning any either. Which is what I was – a nobody; only in those days I still didn't know that, I was full of hopes, and hopes are the opposite of reality.'

'Having hopes isn't bad.'

'Bad or good – that depends on many things; most of all, though, it depends what side you're on. My parents had hoped that there wouldn't be a war and there was; they prayed Franco would lose, but he won; they were confident the Allies would get rid of him after getting rid of Hitler, and he stayed on in the Pardo Palace for forty years. Poor them – them and all the others; poor all of us, who think a thousand hopes and a leaky canteen will see us through a jungle. I too convinced myself that going to Panama would be a step forward, a way of getting to Cecilia for good; back then, I imagined it with such intensity that at times I think of it now as though I were remembering it, as though it really happened. I made a fortune in Panama, I had my own clothes factory or maybe my own furniture business; Cecilia and I got married on a September morning, in Cartago, in the Basilica of Our Lady of the Angels; we spent our honeymoon in Guanacaste, where we had a house on Playa Grande, by the shores of the Pacific Ocean; there are dozens of photographs which show the two of us walking along the sandy beaches in Bahía Culebra and Playa Flamingo, sitting at a restaurant table in Sámara, strolling through the streets of El Coco and Nosara.'

'Are there photographs?'

'No, not really. None of that ever happened. I had another life, not that it was bad, but . . . well, it's as if circumstances somehow forced me to accept a sort of second version of myself. Do you understand? An alternative version. Sometimes you wonder *what would have happened if* . . . and you ask yourself what that would have been like. I loved your grandmother, Aitana, I loved her with almost all my heart. I can't say more than that. But only with almost all my heart.'

94

'What happened to Cecilia?'

'We were very happy during my time in Costa Rica. She was so . . . so perfect. Did I tell you a friend of mine used to call her "the Isosceles Woman"?'

'Eh . . . yes, I think so.'

'And you know what *isosceles* means?'

'It's a triangle.'

'Yes, but it also means "That which has legs of exactly equal lengths".'

'Everybody has legs of equal length.'

'Yes, but not *everybody's* are quite so beautiful. In any case, that little joke was only a way of explaining her . . . well, her proportions.' Truman could find no other word to render the harmony which her features combined, establishing miraculous connections between the jet-black hair and the honey-coloured eyes that had a drop of gorse yellow dissolved in their depths; between the too-thick lips, the slightly aquiline nose and all the other details that came together to form that face's mestizo splendour, with the magical naturalness and precision with which silicone and oxygen crystallize into a beautiful piece of quartz.

'So when you went to work in Panama, what happened to Cecilia?'

'We kept writing to each other, three or four times a week. I was saving most of the money I earned, and learnt my trade as well as I could. Soon my bosses started giving me more responsibilities and raised my wages. Because I was living in a room in the same shop in which I worked, in the Área Colonial, I had almost no expenses. I'd put the money in the bank, bit by bit, and spent my nights repeating the growing total of my savings over and over again, as if the greater my savings the less the distance between me and Cecilia. I could even go without food, and some days only ate a plate of *sancocho*, which is a chicken stew served with rice, fried plantain, and a vegetable called *ñame*, that resembled a potato. It was delicious, and cheap too.'

'What else did you like?'

'Lots of things. My favourites, though, were *carimañola*, which is a cassava stuffed with meat, and *almojábano*, which is corn with cheese. From time to time I also liked to have a glass of Caucho Negro rum or another strong drink called *mataburros*, donkey-killer, which was made with eau-de-vie, honey, and lemon.'

'*Mataburros!*'

'How about that for a name, eh?' Truman's voice had changed now that he was still the boy working in a furniture shop in Panama and was once more far away from Mexico, from that scorching July morning when he would receive a letter from his father asking him to return to Spain and telling him that the lovely Delia had died.

'What did it taste of?'

'At first it was sweet; then it was hell. But you know what? There was an even stronger drink, *cajoba*, a hallucinogenic wine the Indians made, which was said to give you visions and could leave you blind. They made it from the fruit of a palm tree, from a coconut called a *coroso*.'

As he spoke, Truman looked back over more than fifty years to the streets of the Área Colonial and the ruined buildings of Old Panama City, the King's Bridge, the rubble of the old hospital; he got on a tram and began watching the enormous trees go by, the bungalows painted in pastel tones: pink, pale blue, yellow. He passed men in white linen suits, straw hats, with walking sticks, owners of textile factories, who the following Saturday would stop looking serious and impassive for a couple of hours, while they danced polkas to the accompaniment of an orchestra. Why was all that so far in the past and yet so vivid? Why did his memory force him to be present in that way; to walk towards death unable to shrug that burden off, as he advanced with ever greater exhaustion, more and more slowly, like a wounded soldier bearing a second wounded man on his back.

'And you had stopped going to dances like those in Costa Rica?'

'I avoided going anywhere I had to spend money – which meant no bars, no casinos, nothing like that. I even looked for extra work repairing furniture in people's homes or as a typist.'

'Did you type on a typewriter, like Marta?'

'Yes, I had repaired an Underwood I bought in the Central Market in San José, and so I was able to earn some extra money with that. Amongst other things, I transcribed the manuscripts of a Panamanian poet called Esther María Osses, a humanities professor at the university, who apparently once had an affair with the Spanish writer, León Felipe; though of course with all these American films and the poor teaching you get at school nowadays, you won't know who the hell León Felipe was. Esther María Osses. I can see her now, sitting in her office at the university, staring at me with her blue eyes and that slightly tragic expression of hers, so that it always seemed as if she had just got back from visiting graves in a cemetery. Anyway, that's what I was doing in Panama, that and writing to Cecilia, learning all her letters off by heart, going for walks in the Área Colonial, going to the Church of San José ... Have I ever told you about a pirate called Morgan and the Church of San José?'

Of course he had told him, and more than once, as they

both knew full well. Just as they both also knew what Maceo's answer would be.

'Who was Morgan the pirate?' he asked, his excitement betraying how much he was already enjoying the story Truman was about to tell.

'Morgan was one of the most famous buccaneers in history, perhaps the cleverest and most bloodthirsty of them all. Anything he found in his path, he stole – both at sea, where he boarded other ships, and on dry land, where he used the same strategy he used in Panama. He would anchor his ships off the coast of a city and then proceed to destroy it with cannon fire. Once the city was reduced to rubble, he would go ashore and plunder it. You learn exactly the kind of man Henry Morgan was when you see what remains of Old Panama City: a pile of rubble on the shores of the Pacific. However on that occasion, he didn't get everything. You know why?'

'Why?'

'Because the Spaniards tricked him, and though they were much less powerful, they were much cleverer. It was their cunning that saved the Church of San José.'

Truman made another of his melodramatic pauses, glancing round his small room and taking an exasperatingly calm sip from the glass of coffee he drank every night before going to bed.

'How?'

'The church had a solid-gold altar, which they painted over with whitewash, or plaster or something like that. And so Morgan walked past it without even a second glance, before returning to his ship moored off Colombia – thus leaving behind in Panama the most valuable treasure he could ever have stolen. And now, Maceo, I think it's already time for bed.'

The boy stayed sitting right where he was, refusing to believe that the story could come to such an abrupt end.

'And from Panama you went to Mexico? What happened there?'

'Tomorrow. I'll tell you that part tomorrow. And about the trip to El Salvador, how Cecilia and I visited the Quezaltepec volcano, and the waterfalls in Panchimalco, in the Ford her father bought for her. I'll tell you all about it so that it's never forgotten, so . . . and you have to keep it . . .' His eyes were starting to close. '. . . so that it won't be as if it never happened.'

After that the boy went out of the room and Truman stayed there, thinking, just before he fell asleep, about his time in Mexico, about the morning he received the letter that would completely alter the course of his life. 'Poor Delia,' he thought, 'if she had known what a bombshell her death would be, how far it swept me from my dreams.'

But Delia knew neither this nor many other things – just as they did not know and would never know for certain what caused her sudden demise; in what part of her heart the disease that would take her life began to form. Nor did they see her, on a September morning in 1936, entering the house of the Falangists who saved her husband from the firing squad; they did not see her approach that country mansion to which she had been and would again be summoned by her benefactors, dressed in her best clothes, a smile of gratitude on her face, as she carried in a small tray of cakes she had baked herself. Nor did they see her emerge an hour later, a vacant stare in her eyes, which glinted like dirty water – like the eyes of the dead fish she so hated – in the company of two men dressed in identical blue shirts; men who had made her see how complicated her situation remained, who had hinted how easy it would be to put her husband back up against the wall of the football ground from where they had rescued him.

'Yes, indeed,' the first man said, 'the way things stand, though you're not much use for anything else, it has to be said that you Reds certainly know how to suck a cock: right in and swallow.'

And the second man added, laughing:

'Hey, Delia, don't forget to come again, next time you bake some cakes.'

No, Truman never knew about any of this.

Long before she saw him pass her doorway, Marta heard his footfall amid the night-time silence of the apartment – a silence broken only by Samuel's fits of coughing coming from the next bedroom: an increasingly frequent succession of coughs piling up one on top of the other, with a sound so hollow that you imagined a man whose lungs, liver, heart and everything else had been removed. She was therefore able to follow her brother's absurd route in her mind: from Truman's room he only needed to go along the corridor to his right and then turn left to get to his own bedroom, instead of which he went in the opposite direction, passing the main bathroom, the study, the hallway, the kitchen and, finally, his sister's and parents' bedrooms. In other words, he went the longest way round once more.

The consequences of the lightning which struck the boy had proved so strange that none of the various doctors Ruth took him to see were able to offer an opinion, or find anywhere in their tests, X-rays or electroencephalograms the slightest trace of an explanation for those unprecedented symptoms. Hence it had been impossible to prescribe a remedy: what medicines or prescriptions were there to cure an illness that did not exist? Marta thought that it was up to Maceo himself to clarify the matter, perhaps intuitively, and that this was why he had recently been so obsessed by anything to do with the sky, spent hours looking at the stars through his binoculars, and avidly read anything he could find about space in the newspapers or in the books given to him by Truman – who in her view was always far too inclined to encourage a knowledge of trivia and unwanted ideas. One day, while Maceo was at school, she had glanced through these books and had been astonished to learn that the Earth performed two types of movement – vertical and lateral rotation; that Saturn, Uranus, Jupiter, and Neptune were composed of hydrogen and had a lower average density than water; that the satellite orbiting Pluto was called Charon; and that Mercury had a core of liquid iron. That is what she gathered from the first book, yet the second seemed even odder: it was a book about storms, divided into sections with titles such as 'The Johnstown Flood', 'The Great Lakes Hurricane', 'The Flooding of the Big Thompson River', 'The Great Frost of '83' and 'The Bay of Bengal Cyclone'. What sort of an effect would stories like that have on a boy of Maceo's age, she wondered, along with all the others he was continually hearing from his grandfather, all that talk of the Civil War and Central America, volcanoes, earthquakes, exile? Not for the first time, she felt amazed at her parents' inability to check the unhealthy influence exerted by Truman over the boy.

She went out into the corridor, where she stood for a long while outside his door, listening until she heard Maceo get into bed and turn out the light. Afterwards, back in her own room, sitting in the dark in the small oil-blue vinyl armchair which Samuel had given her for passing her second-year exams with good grades the previous year, she returned her attention to her own matters, to pondering the decision she was about to take.

Everything had happened so fast, and in such an impromptu manner, that she was no longer quite sure why she had acted the way she had, nor whether she was now on the point of rushing towards something, or rather was being dragged towards it. Events took place in the following sequence on the night she and Lucas watched the passage of the comet together, just as she had dreamt they would. As soon as they arrived at the house in the woods, she and Iraide lost no time in ditching Enara. At first, Marta could see no sign of Lucas amid the young men and women all drinking Cuba libres and moving lazily in time to the obscure songs popular with that cliquish crowd, who liked to think they never strayed far from the fringes of commercial music – *hey, it's so, like, boring, you know, so predictable*. The Dream Syndicate, Tricky, Sonic Youth, P.J. Harvey; that was what they were dancing to.

The weather was unsettled and chill, except in the grounds of the party where Lucas and some friends had had the foresight to section off an area by the front porch with half a dozen empty oil drums filled with wood and coal. These served both as incinerators and as heaters, providing not only makeshift outdoor heating but also a place to throw away the inflammable waste generated by the guests: paper cups and plates, empty cigarette packets, wrappers. Beyond the wreaths of smoke rising from these small bonfires the night lay cold and dark, and the air was as clear and sharp as the blade of an axe.

In search of Lucas, Marta wandered among the guests, or prowled through the woods, all the while feeling progressively worn down by jealousy and hurt by his absence. Occasionally, she caught sight of unexpected objects lying on the snow that remained under the pine trees: an empty fuel can, the frame of a bicycle and, unlikeliest of all, a pair of rubber sandals so out of place amid that icy landscape that it was as though they were there solely as proof that before the winter there really had been a summer – a time of ice-cream parlours and swimming pools, of days when men were still unshaven at noon.

Most of the guests had remained in the area at the front of the house, where they were dancing to the industrial sounds and hermetic beats of songs she found she recognised, almost always without meaning to. Seen from a distance, the dancers formed a shapeless mass, a hundred-headed being which moved in an endless succession of waves and spasms as though wounded or about to shed a skin. Marta imagined what the future for those people might hold: in a few years' time one of the girls would marry a footballer, one of the boys would be sent to prison for tax evasion, another would drown off the coast of Formentera; two would become very rich, two others would die of cancer. That's what would happen, although she also wondered which bit was meant for whom.

'Mental ischemia,' said a voice at her side, suddenly. It was Iraide.

'What?'

'The blood flow – it doesn't reach his brain,' she said, jerking her thumb back at a student who stood a few metres away, a foolish grin on his face. As if to say 'Cheers,' he raised the bottle he was holding. 'Isn't he wonderful? With his lumberjack shirt and that look about him that says "I spend every Monday afternoon playing darts." I just love these idiots: they're so big and yet they're so easy to ignore!'

Marta responded with a weak smile and lit a cigarette to hide her lack of enthusiasm for the joke. After a couple of drags, though, she remembered Lucas and put it out, not wanting to taste of cigarettes when she eventually found him. 'Mental ischemia' was one of a number of private jokes she and Iraide employed when they wanted to talk in

104

public without other people being able to understand. The code was based on terms learnt in their medical studies: in the presence of a student who was none too bright they would declare 'lethargic encephalitis', their faces a mask of feigned seriousness; in the case of someone they considered malicious their usual verdict would be 'vascular uraemia' – or 'multiple tympanites' if, rather than evil, their victim was merely fat. Their diagnosis of Enara, for example, usually took the form of a conversation of this kind:

Marta: 'What did I tell you?'

Iraide: 'Really? In that case, it's just as we feared.'

Marta: 'Acute otosclerosis: she really can't understand a thing we say.'

For some reason it was then that Marta realised she had forgotten the records Enara suggested she bring. In any case, Beck would perhaps have been fine in that context, but not Oasis.

'So there we were,' Iraide went on, still beside her, 'chatting about how the comet would pass in two hours' time, right, and I start telling him about the gaseous core, the trail, and all the rest of it, while this guy just stands there looking at me as if I were the hieroglyphic symbol for a cow. And then guess what he comes out with? Listen, it's wonderful. He goes and says: "Hey, what's with all the mumbo-jumbo!" Can you believe it? Mumbo-jumbo! And then he put a hand on my arse. Dear God, how sweet! He's from Palencia, studies Management Sciences, and he's got one the size of a baguette.'

'How would you know?'

'Ah, well . . . I had to put my hands somewhere while he was touching my arse. Anyway, my dear, I'm off to have some fun.'

'With him or at his expense?'

'What exactly is that supposed to mean? You must think I'm completely heartless . . . At his expense, *naturally*.'

They both laughed and exchanged a brief kiss on the lips in parting. Marta watched her walk away: a slim yet solidly built woman, with a touch of the athlete about her. Though undoubtedly beautiful, Iraide perhaps possessed the kind of beauty that was a little too severe, despite a body which, in her own words, would please one man in a thousand . . . and drive the other 999 wild: a firm body that had a hint of listlessness, which men found both exciting and somewhat daunting, although Marta herself did not think this a very attractive quality.

'Men are such fools,' Iraide would say, 'they're so brutish and yet so feeble that they only ever fall into two categories – horny or scared. They're simply not made any other way. There is no third species. Just those two and that's it. Men all suffer from irreversible anomaly, pronounced polio, and chronic psychopathology. Either they're trying to stick it in someone or else they're obsessed with their pathetic worries – *I think mine's too small, I'll be bald in five or six years' time* – and all that shit.'

That evening, Marta predicted as she scanned the middle distance, once more on the lookout for Lucas, Iraide would have her fun with the student from Palencia until she got bored with him; as usual she would only go as far as she wanted to, before at a stroke taking back all that she had granted, abolishing his acquired rights at will, the way a queen can repeal a law or revoke a safe conduct.

At last, on one side of the house, standing by the kitchen door, surrounded by a small circle of eight or nine others, who for some reason seemed to want to keep to the sidelines, away from other people – which instead of rendering them any more invisible or discreet only made them stand out all the more, due to that aura of mystery that always envelops those stood on the edge of a cliff or the line of a frontier – Lucas appeared. She went pale when she recognised two of the people he was with: Enara and Luisa, the girl he had supposedly been with in the hotel.

It was so hard to remain standing, so easy to lose balance: the mere sight of Luisa – her long red hair, her brightly coloured outfit – and the glimpse of the evil she caught in Enara's gaze were enough for all Marta's plans to crumble away in an instant, for her self-confidence to vanish, and for the speech she had prepared to be altered wildly by an awful, invisible hand that left out entire sentences and swapped some words for others that sounded similar but meant the opposite: security–insecurity, arrogance–dance–disgrace, valour–pallor–terror. It was in this state, furious but unarmed, that she went up to Lucas.

'Hey! Look who's here!' Enara's voice had changed and now came from a greater height, from inside a person more confident and far more powerful than her. Her tone of voice and dilated pupils told Marta exactly what Lucas and his clan had been doing while she had been looking for him.

'Well, well,' Luisa said, 'so you are . . . Now, what was I going to say . . . Oh yes, of course! You're here.'

It was obvious from the way they all laughed that the others found those incoherent phrases extremely funny; all except Lucas, who was staring at Marta, his face oddly serious. Luisa slipped her arms round him and stared back at Marta: the way someone, after locking the gates to their mansion, stares out at an unlit street, feeling safe amid the darkness of their own garden, the family dogs at their heels. Marta wondered what was the way to force those bars apart, wrench the padlock open.

'Hey, darling,' said Lucas, finally. 'You're looking good tonight.'

'I came to fetch you; so say goodbye to these people now and come with me,' she replied sharply, forgetting the various opening gambits she had prepared in advance and opting for the most direct route between where she was and where she wanted to go. At first, she was alarmed by her own surliness and the vehemence with which the words came out; but on seeing how Luisa instinctively hugged herself closer to Lucas, Marta realised that the blow had struck home, and she was glad to have acted the way she did – in fights, you have to find a way to make your opponent fear you, something that will turn their fear into part of your strength.

'Good heavens!' Enara interjected. 'How vulgar – calling us *these people*! Or perhaps you don't know our names? Well, this is Julia, and this is Luisa, who you already know . . .'

'Hey, Enara,' Marta cut in, 'what's with the bad imitation of Iraide? You're not trying to patronise me, are you? Because if you are, you won't just need a tongue, you'll also need a brain.'

Shut up! – she ordered herself, but only inside her head. She had to calm down, rein in all the panic, hysteria, desire, and hatred, and find a way of coping with them somehow. 'Get him away from here what the hell do I care about Enara concentrate my God concentrate on Lucas only Lucas my God just worry about him *please*.'

In the course of that week, she had been tormented by such devastating doubts that she was now starting to feel the effects of so many options, suspicions, and questions, all of which led time and again to the same conclusion: she could not live without Lucas. And true though it was that the struggle between her hopes and her misgivings had split her into two opposing Martas, that one of these had wanted to warn and convince the other what a big mistake total surrender to Lucas would be, there was also no doubting that of the two, this cautious, sensible half was the weaker.

Her own troubles apart, during that period Marta had also had to bear a share of the crushing weight of her own family; a percentage of what had become an almost unbearable burden in the wake of the upheavals caused by Maceo's accident and Samuel's illness within a group of people who were increasingly growing apart and, it seemed, going through a phase of self-destruction. This critical juncture was made all the worse by her own uncertainties and Ruth's altered state – Ruth, in whom she had begun to see a new, unpredictable and enigmatic woman emerge. Marta knew that matters were not going well between her parents, but as all she could see were specific portions or certain segments of the overall problem, the lure of a future with Lucas grew in direct proportion to the dwindling appeal of her home. And so in her own blurred view of the facts, Lucas was not the danger but the person who combined all the answers.

So much so that on Monday, as she was on her way out of the secretarial college, when the centre manager came up to her to resume the conversation they had postponed from Friday, Marta had a moment's hesitation when she found out what it concerned: it was the offer of a job, to work as secretary in a clinic, on a reasonable salary, with the prospect of promotion within the company, and a nine-to-three schedule that would allow her to continue her studies if she attended lectures at the university in the afternoons. Of course, that was precisely the opposite of what she wanted; it was the kind of compromise her father had always seemed, in some way, to be pushing her to accept – don't rely only on your own steam, follow the paths that others take, be happy with what you find even if it means forgetting what you set out to look for in the first place. It went without saying that Marta had no intention of accepting the job, but at the thought of the salary, she did allow herself to imagine life with Lucas in an apartment of their own, combining their studies with a matrimonial bliss full of love and companionship, of little adventures and mutual support.

At the time, as she walked under recently lit street lamps on her way home to her parents' apartment, she had laughed at herself for having such thoughts; but now, a few days later, sitting on the oil-blue armchair in her bedroom and recalling the events of the evening of Lucas's party, she was a good deal more serious. For that had been the night when, on seeing how the boy was slipping through her fingers and how futile her attempts to retain him were, she had decided to accept the job for his sake; she would offer him a life of tranquility and independence in which he could continue his studies and she would make sure that she earned enough to support him: just think, our very own home, just the two of us, no one else, free to do whatever we like, the whole world ours for the taking.

She grew a great deal more serious as she remembered that he had agreed, and that on her return to the secretarial college the next day, she would have to decide between accepting the job or losing Lucas. 'Perhaps it's not so hard, after all, to combine a working life with a degree course; I'd only have to give up six hours a day, lots of people manage it; in some ways afternoons are better; besides, it will only be a temporary measure, a halfway house, something to stop him coming and going like a radio signal at every tunnel.'

She could not get the boy out of her mind, the image of the two of them in the woods, holding hands, looking up; she could not forget his eyes, as hard and beautiful as diamonds, as he watched the comet progress across the sky. She could not turn her back on all that; she realised this in the course of her confrontation with Luisa and Enara, when she told Lucas to come with her and he replied:

'What d'you want?'

That was all he said, *what d'you want*, not moving from Luisa's side, with that sleepy glow in his eyes – God knew what they'd been taking indoors – looking her up and down, because you're so pretty tonight, darling, *what d'you want*, those three words now prowling about inside her mind, making a shocking, sombre sound, *what d'you want*, the sound of funeral bells, of dogs tipping over a bin. Marta still remembered the distress she had felt in those instants, the feeling of emptiness, of sinking, the feeling that she was being torn apart – fusiform, plane, orbicular muscles – reduced to ashes.

Afterwards it stopped. Afterwards everything was different, and as she stood in the clearing in the woods, staring up at the heavens, Lucas at her side, she thought about the other guests at that party, about how stupid and cowardly they all were. She saw them once again from the same perspective as before, as though they were already in the future but she were still here: the girl who was going to marry a footballer led an ill-fated life, full of misfortune and loneliness, afflicted by the sort of paralysis that traps those who spend their time thinking not about what to do to start their life again but about what they had done to ruin it; the future fraudster spent years obsessed with money, and always fondly remembered the wonderful girl he had met at university whom he hadn't had the courage to marry at all costs, by telling himself to hell with what's sensible, think of what you care about, not what's convenient.

But nothing like that would happen to her. Of that she was certain. Her mind was made up: she would accept the secretarial post at the clinic. She closed her eyes and told herself that rather than forfeiting something, she was gaining something. She promised herself that the next morning would mark the dawn of an age of splendour, the start of the road to a new life. From the facts at our disposal, it would not be absurd to suppose that she saw herself moving along it from north to south with irrepressible determination, her demeanour dignified and majestic.

'It all started on the night of the comet,' she would tell some of her old friends in a few years' time, perhaps Iraide and other friends she had now; they would all know exactly what she meant, for that event had been a key date in their lives too, a kind of landmark by which to set your bearings: 'Pablo and I met in the month of the comet'; 'Remember Laura – the girl who died in a train crash a few weeks after the passage of the comet?'

Poor Marta, with her hopes and her landmark, moving from north to south, so majestic, so unheeding, like a tiger padding towards a trap.

CHAPTER FOUR

I

Samuel shuffled back several paces and raised his free hand, raised it as high as it would go, fingers wide apart, palm upright and pointing away from his face, in a gesture that seemed both a sign of peace and a plea for mercy; on the men still restraining him, however, his pleas appeared to have little effect, and while one took an even firmer hold of his arm, the other started slapping him again, this time with such force that Samuel was knocked to the ground. Samuel's first thought, though, was not for the scorching pain – it was for the mud staining his suit, and for an explanation he could use to justify it, if he had to.

'. . . you – great – big . . .' the second man said, giving Samuel several kicks in the stomach, pacing his words to coincide with his kicks, like a teacher showing a child how to count syllables: '. . . dir – ty – ba – stard.'

Afterwards they moved slowly off, walking backwards, shouting *you pervert, bastard, come here again and you're dead*; and as he watched them walk away down the wet street, Samuel prayed that it had all been only a bad dream and that the feel of the dirty rainwater against his skin or the sharp pain in his side – not in fact the result of any attack, but merely bad posture – would cause him to wake up in his own bed.

Of course, Samuel knew that this was impossible and that the whole thing – the mud, the abuse, the kicks and slaps – was nothing less than what it seemed: he had just been beaten up.

It happened after work, not far from his office at the steelworks on the outskirts of the city, when instead of waiting for the bus that took him on an interminably slow route home every evening, he had, almost automatically, begun to follow a woman in the street. What made him single her out? He wasn't sure. Perhaps there was no reason. The woman was probably about forty, blonde, and wore a green raincoat. What else? She looked scared, most of all she looked scared – at least that was the impression he gained from seeing her quick nervous steps, the way she kept glancing left and right and over her shoulder as though she felt cornered or was running away.

He had begun to follow her almost as a joke, almost with a kind of reluctance, expecting that she too would halt at the bus stop; but she hadn't, and instead she had kept walking until she came to the most secluded part of that district, to an area where there were no shops or tenement blocks and where she entered a park, Samuel still in pursuit. He felt certain that she had noticed him, and the thought of this excited him as much as it had on the other occasions, provoking in him a feverish sense of pleasure, an arousal that came with the knowledge that he was feared, powerful.

There was no one else in the park. The lighting was poor and the presence of rusty sleds and broken swings served only to accentuate the cold. Samuel quickened his pace, until he was so close to the woman that he could hear the words going through her mind: I'm going to die, what does he want, perhaps he's only after some money, to die like an animal, out in the cold, he's going to rape me, dear God, what does he want from me? Samuel kept the game up for a little longer, wondering if she had children, where she lived, what her name was, whether it was Fátima or

116

Alicia, Lourdes or Carmen or Lola. He still believed that as soon as she started running he would let her get away, like he had the others, but when, on turning out of the park, she did so, he sprinted after her and caught up with her on an area of waste ground.

Now, as he sat up and tried to clean the mud from his suit, he remembered the way she had spun round all of a sudden; the look of terror on her face, her shrill voice panting:

'Who are you? Just tell me who you are and . . . leave me alone, just tell me what you want. Here . . .' – she thrust a hand inside her bag, pulled out a purse; her hands shook as she offered him some notes. 'Have them – these are for you, just let me go.'

'Hey, what are you talking about? You don't understand, I don't . . .' As Samuel took a step towards her she tried to scratch him, before running off again, but he was able to catch up with her a little further on; they struggled wordlessly, grabbing each other by the arm, by the wrist. . . . you've got this all wrong, I'm telling you.'

'Help! Help me, please!'

'Don't shout! I'm not going to hurt you!'

At which point the two men had appeared. And other people too – maybe seven or eight others. Where had they come from? He didn't know. Perhaps he had chased her for longer than he realised after she ran off the second time, after offering him the notes; now he could see two or three nearby buildings, and a telephone box, a stretch of pavement.

'What were you doing, eh? You bastard!' With the words came the shoves, the struggling.

'Nothing! I only wanted to . . . I was just . . .'

'Keep hold of him! Let's get the police!'

'You were just . . . You were just what?' Someone was shaking him violently, someone else had grabbed him by the hair.

'He was going to kill me. I managed to run away then . . . he wanted to rape me.'

'To rape her, eh? Is that right, pig? Why don't you try raping me instead? Scumbag!'

'Uggh! Stop! Leave me alone. I wasn't . . . I didn't . . .'

'Get the police! Someone go and call the police!'

Then came more blows, the slipping in the mud, the kicks and the insults, the obscene gestures, the sense of shame. But no one went off to make any phone calls.

Samuel wandered along empty streets until the sound of traffic led him to a main road. He intended to flag down a taxi, but fares were so high, it would work out so expensive, that he decided to take the bus instead.

It seemed the few passers-by he met were all staring at him: to them he was a strange being, covered in sores and bruises; a repulsive creature more usually encountered in swamps or dungeons. He walked quickly, taking long strides in an effort to shake that monster off, crossing from one side of the road to the other in search of the bus stop. He wanted to get away from there; he wanted to go home, leave that enormous, all-encompassing pain behind. 'What happened back there marked the end of something,' he told himself. 'I'm not feeling well – that's what the matter is. It's been these last few weeks, this constant churning in my stomach, the cramps, the retching, the nausea. From now on, I'm going to put everything right – with Ruth, with the kids, with Truman.'

With Marta too; and he remembered her ridiculous idea of working in a clinic, moving to her own apartment. 'I'll deal with her first. I'll . . .' He took a deep breath in an attempt to overcome his tiredness. '. . . I'll explain to her how hard things really are; she thinks . . .' He took another deep breath: he was now gasping. '. . . she thinks it's all so easy, and that having to pay your own way will be no different from having everything handed to you on a plate.'

And so he began to rehearse the conversation that he would have with Marta the following evening, in the way he always did – as if she were there the next day after dinner, listening to him, and he was in both moments simultaneously, in the now and the then. 'Listen, my girl,' he started off by saying, 'it seems to me there are a couple of things you have yet to learn. No, just listen! Please don't interrupt. And please *never ever* forget how much I love you. Never forget that, no matter what happens. Don't forget it – or you'll be making a big mistake. Don't forget it, because that lies at the heart of what I'm about to say next.'

While pondering this, engaged in the elaborate preparation of a speech that would have all the hallmarks of a cleric's or a statesman's – like those he had often made at university – he gradually detached himself from everything that had just taken place, until the events themselves became distant, hazy: the woman in the green raincoat, the area of open ground, the blows that were landing in already distant corners of his life. Had all that really happened?

Though he did not feel guiltless, he did feel somewhat more resolute, as if he had just knocked down a tower that had been about to collapse.

Rat poison is what Ruth had been adding to Samuel's food, a small dose to soups and vegetables, a somewhat larger dose in casseroles. It was inconceivable even to her that she could have been capable of such a thing, that she had ever reached that stage – hitherto unknown territory. For until then, each time she read in the newspapers about one of those fairly frequent cases of murderous house-wives and homemade poisons made from insecticides, cleaning products, or complex cocktails of medication, such occurrences had always struck her as belonging to another world, as being news to do with people of an entirely different race, people with sombre feelings and basic instincts who inhabited the darkest recesses of soci-ety, and whose actions filled the crime pages of certain newspapers with pictures of blood-spattered kitchens and gun-wounds incurred at point-blank range.

For Ruth, turning herself into one of these women had been a kind of game, especially at first: on the night of the comet she came home in an awful state, feeling so shat-tered and defiled by her latest rendezvous with Ramón that while preparing the supper, she began to wonder what effect her suicide would have. She saw her children after her death, walking back from the funeral, their faces disfigured by an all-embracing, ineluctable grief. It was a grey morning as they slowly made their way from the church, in silence, in the rain, still unable to believe that when they got back to the apartment Ruth would not be there somewhere, like she always was, perhaps sitting in one of the armchairs in the living room, reading the newspaper. Marta was staring provocatively at Samuel, her eyes seemingly full of disdain; Truman kept shaking his head in sorrow: 'I can't believe it, she was so young, who'd have guessed it, how awful.' Maceo had a flower in one hand, and Ruth wondered whether it was one of the same flowers that had been lain on her grave, a keepsake he would treasure with such pure and unconditional love that it provoked in her a sadness akin to joy: comforting but frightening, sweet yet bitter too.

She was in this nervous, depressed state – engulfed by all the shame, worry, anger, and bewilderment, mulling over the whys, hows and with whoms of the situation – when Samuel came in and began to badger her.

'See? You're frying it – why do you always fry everything; why not grill it instead? Your way works out twice as expensive and far more unhealthy: the oil raises your cholesterol levels, damages the heart . . .'

Ruth stared down at the frying pan; inside were two fish which, as they cooked, were turning from the colour of silver to that of marble. They now seemed mysterious, unrecognisable creatures, the repositories, perhaps, of a magical or esoteric message. She thought of a counter-attack that would break through Samuel's siege: 'And miserliness – what does that lead to? Paranoia?' But, in truth, she did not really feel under siege. She was about to resort to the joke her father would have made: 'And would Sir like anything else?' But neither was she in the mood for that.

From silver to marble, from gloss to matt – just like her life, just like her own squalid existence with all its troubles and smothered fires, an existence in which she could go neither forwards nor backwards. She was caught at the worst of all possible junctures – the one where plans for the future were banned, and remembering your hopes was as depressing and useless as remembering your dead. What could she do, then? Leave her home and lose everything? Scuttle the ship, as her father would have said? But to do that, she needed gunpowder and her own boat to sink. And Ruth was of the opinion that she had neither.

Her thoughts returned to the period when they had both just finished their studies and Samuel had asked her to marry him. Married? The two of them? Whatever became of that couple, she with the degree in physics, he a qualified chemical engineer, both of them ambitious and, in her opinion, special; both ready to conquer the world wrapped only in their own aura, ready to share out the spoils of a perfect life?

Through Truman, Samuel found a job in the admin department of a steelworks owned by an old Republican friend of his father. It was intended to be a temporary measure, an instant recipe for being both together and self-sufficient, something which, according to Samuel, they would come to refer to in time as 'the etcetera etcetera part of our lives'.

But that was not what happened. Nor was that job the start of any kind of ascent; instead it was the end of everything, it was what triggered off her mediocre existence, for Samuel never did manage to leave that steelworks on the outskirts of the city, and she could never forget that glittering world she dreamt of and which she lost in the cruellest way possible: irretrievably, and before it was ever hers. How far could two people who were trapped go? Ruth knew the answer to that.

What she did not know, however, was the reason. What she never found out, then or later, was why Samuel gave up on himself, why he toppled himself with such an unprecedented absence of pity that it led her to think that perhaps the rest of him – his talent for leadership, the way he seemed born to succeed – was the part that had always been false, a sham.

Whatever the explanation, the fact was that the more immersed in the world of work and responsibilities he became, the more the rest of his aspirations were gradually left behind, left to slowly collapse and crumble away, becoming part of a dynamic whereby it was impossible both to grow and consolidate at the same time. Soon he was promoted, his salary raised – and likewise his fear of having it taken away. His next step had been to convince Ruth of the need to buy an apartment: how about it, think of it as a starting point, the way things are at the moment paying rent makes no sense, an apartment would be something of our own, a place to come home to, it would mean security, for the both of us.

Time and again she had said yes to this other man, an unreserved yes to the marriage, a yes without a second thought to the apartment; for at that moment the other man was still there, embodied in Samuel, and endorsing each of her decisions. His credit remained good even when he started to lose contact with certain influential spheres – such as the private universities, the Socialist Party – which had attracted some of his fellow students and which Samuel had categorically predicted would have no future. And he also held back when two or three of these old university friends, whom he dismissed as too impatient, too opportunist, began to make a name for themselves in political circles or joined certain companies or associations, at a time when he was still maintaining that it was too soon, that it was early days as yet, and better to let oneself be overtaken by those who would then be the first to fall. He proved wrong about almost everything, of course, and so conclusively that all Samuel's moderation brought them was a resounding defeat: those who had once seemed ready to follow wherever he led now gave him a wide berth and generally treated him with a pitiless, crushing scorn, perhaps because to most people a failed hero was far worse than a mere failure. Among their number was Ruth, for deep down, this was exactly what she thought too.

That was not how it had been in the beginning, though. In the beginning she had felt flattered by the way Samuel seemed to place her so firmly above everything else – 'first, come what may,' as he himself used to say: what non-negotiable, all-powerful love! Then things changed, when Ruth first began to suspect that what he was offering her was not so much an ascent to the summit of a mountain as a life down in the foothills and a share of the same fate. One day, it suddenly occurred to her that some of those students whose future Samuel had predicted would be so bleak – 'Poor old Luis, just how far does he think he'll get if every time he opens his mouth he sounds like a village priest?'; 'What do I think of Paula? I have yet to understand why *Paula* and *incompetence* are two different words' – would eventually become influential people, whom sooner or later she and Samuel would see rising above their lives, with the jealous gaze of those who remain on the ground, those people at airports who watch the planes taking off. And Ruth was right. She also came to realise that Samuel never would leave that factory which recycled steel, and she was right about that too: for a period he worked in the offices and then, in the mid-eighties, he was transferred to the laboratory, where he was still working fifteen years later, testing for traces of nuclear waste and radioactive leaks among the tons of scrap metal destined to become domestic appliances, tools, or building materials.

'The responsibility is enormous,' Samuel would tell her, 'simply because of the large number of dangerous isotopes that exist: caesium-137, cobalt-60 . . . allow them to go undetected and it could mean disaster. Remember, they could end up as almost anything, even the most harmless-looking object, like a chair or a fork. In Taiwan, not so long ago, they built an apartment block using girders contaminated with cobalt-60, and for over twenty years all 114 residents were exposed to harmful radiation, in doses as high as 120 microsieverts per hour.'

Ruth did not at all see things in this light, however – to her this was no honourable duty, no great responsibility, it was just an ordinary job, and a boring way to spend one's days. All she saw was an ugly factory on the edge of the city, with huge furnaces for melting metal, and lorries loaded with scrap iron parked outside. And she could imagine the opposite – all the things which she had expected to possess but did not, and which Paula did; Paula who may have been so incompetent but who was also so famous, and no doubt rich; or in the hands of Luis, who perhaps spoke like a village priest but had become chairman of a multinational company. There it all was, lodged in every empty corner of her modest apartment: someone's garden, someone else's sauna, the greenhouses, the garages, the pergolas, the swimming pools. And it was precisely into one of these swimming pools that Ruth dived, from her own second-class home, to swim a while in the dark, like she did every evening when the weather was warm in the life she never had; underwater, amid that other-worldly silence so conducive to unusual memories, she remembered Samuel, a chemistry student she had gone out with at university who had wanted to marry her. She remembered him well: an intelligent, somewhat formal boy, of average height, with an untrustworthy voice and deep swamp-green eyes. What became of him? Where was he now? What became of him after she turned him down? What would have happened to the two of them had she not preferred Luis?

On returning to reality Ruth realised that Samuel had left the kitchen, no doubt after seeing her lost in thought, staring down at those two symbolic fish, which – as ordinary, everyday sole once more – were now burning in the frying pan. She turned off the gas and tipped the inedible dinner into the bin, knowing that as soon as her husband discovered wastefulness of such magnitude it would spark off another row; this put her on her guard in advance and sent the rage surging through her, wave upon wave until there seemed to be nothing else. Like someone hearing the approach of a barking dog, she could feel it more and more keenly: the shouts, the accusations, the toxic words, the constant slights; and then the anger, the two of them there in bed, the atmosphere of their bedroom charged with electricity, full of a hatred that could almost be seen shining out from among the shadows, the way St Elmo's fire appeared amid the masts of a ship after a storm.

She had thought about killing herself; but why should it be her? Why not Samuel? She began to plot her crime, though more in jest than anything else. She hunted out the box with the rat poison she had once sprinkled around the apartment, prompted by thoughts of the butcher's below, that place full of blood and germs – a source, she imagined, of innumerable infections. Then, for some reason, she thought about Maceo, about the countless stories of storms and lightning which everybody had started telling him all of a sudden or which were now frequently featured on television and in the newspapers. Was it coincidence or had they always been there? The first bolt of lightning had struck a woman in Málaga, just as she was leaving a grocery: Sara L.A. suffered no serious injuries, though her clothes caught fire and she was left completely naked in broad daylight, with all her shopping (the way Ruth imagined it) scattered around her – fruit, yogurts, tins. The second bolt of lightning struck the father of an acquaintance of hers, in a park in León, while he strolled under some trees with his two greyhounds. The third wiped out an entire Colombian – or was it Kenyan? – football team, though it left all their eleven opponents unharmed. The fourth struck a female pharmacist from Seville who survived, though she was left with after-effects as inexplicable as those affecting Maceo, who slept for hours without moving a muscle and always went everywhere via the longest route. The lightning caught the woman unawares, as she was drawing down the metal shutters of her pharmacy – where was that, wondered Ruth: near the Guadalquivir, in Calle Sierpes, in the Triana district? Since then, she had lost all sense of hot and cold, and now needed someone beside her at all times, to taste her food or test the bathwater, to adjust the heating or to decide what clothes she ought to put on each morning, depending on the changes in the weather.

Ruth lifted the lid off the box of poison while she strolled leisurely through the streets of Seville, ten years earlier, over the Easter holidays; and it was as she left behind the Tower of Gold, the Archive of the Indies, the Parliament building, the House of Pilate, and the Giralda bell tower, that she picked up the plate with Samuel's vegetables.

A little later, when the whole family was gathered together around the table, she set the same plate down in front of Samuel. All she wanted to do was teach him a lesson, cause him some harmless pain. She looked at him sitting there in his striped pyjamas, and almost burst out laughing as she remembered that this poor man was the person who was going to make all her dreams come true. Because she and Samuel were both so special, so different, they lived in an ideal world – unicorns romped through their forests, while in other people's there were only hares. She felt sorry for herself, but also for Samuel. During their honeymoon in New York, he had given her an atlas and they had stuck little green flags in all the places they were going to visit: Ceylon, Madagascar, the Fiji Islands, Samoa. As well as remembering the destinations, she even remembered what she had imagined about each one: the bamboo fields, the tropical beaches, the orangey light of the afternoons.

'I'm going to try and do things your way,' she said, hoping her voice sounded neutral, uninflected. 'I've cooked your vegetables using a cheaper, soya-based oil. See if you like it. You may find it tastes more . . . more bitter.'

Samuel tried some, and said:

'Hmm. Yes, well . . . it's different, no doubt about that. But I wouldn't say it tastes bad,' and then he smiled, for he could see that his marriage was going to survive, and that with the kind of good faith Ruth had just shown they'd be able to sort everything out, stitch up all of their wounds.

Whoever said that you couldn't change horses in mid-stream?

'Remember', Ruth said, 'when we were in New York, how you wanted to go to Samoa to see the tomb of Robert Louis Stevenson?'

Samuel smiled at her again. How nice that matters had started to patch themselves up over that very dinner, he thought to himself, the dinner on the night of the comet.

'At times I dreamt of finding a hoard of treasure, one valuable enough to bring Cecilia back within my grasp. Don't look at me like that – when you live in Central America you realise that's not at all as far-fetched as it sounds . . . Remember, over there, it's a different world . . . there's even a place in Peru called Infierno, Hell – how about that then? It's on the edge of a jungle which the conquistadors named Madre de Dios, Mother of God. Through it runs a river in which there are eels capable of producing electric shocks of over 400 volts. See what I mean? Hard though it may be to believe, in that part of the world there really are giant eels and secret treasures.'

'Of course – because of all the ships sunk by Henry Morgan.'

'That's not the real reason, though it's true some treasure-hunters did find vast riches that had been stashed away by the pirates; no, it was because of the hundreds of Spanish and Portuguese ships that had sunk, over the centuries, all along the coast. The caravels used by the conquistadors, that sort of thing. There were countless legends, you know, but they all had the same ending: an impassable reef, and a dozen or more chests full of gold and precious stones lying at the bottom of the ocean, just waiting for someone to go down and find them.'

'But were these legends or was it true?' Maceo asked.

'That depends on whether or not any chests of treasure were ever found,' Truman replied. 'And believe me' – his voice had now taken on a confiding tone – '. . . many were.'

'Do you know any stories?'

'Of course I do. There are lots of them, and some still await an ending. For example, there was a Spanish frigate called the *Juno*, which sank off the coast of Virginia; all four hundred crew died, except for seven sailors who had gone in search of help and boarded an American ship shortly before their own ship sank, and a boy who was later washed up on the island of Chincoteague, tied to a piece of timber.'

'Almost like Moses in the Nile.'

'Almost. Except they didn't call this boy Moses, they called him James Alone.'

'What happened to him? Did he go back to Spain?'

'No, he didn't. He grew up among the island's inhabitants, married several times, and had so many children that nowadays you'll find hundreds of his descendants living there. Although in fact, James Alone was not the only thing which the tides brought to those shores; because dozens of ships sank in that bay, where the *galernas* were so fierce and the . . .'

'What's a *galerna*?'

'A wind, a squally wind. Anyway, it was in that very spot, a century earlier, that a ship called the *Galga* went down. The sole survivors were half a dozen horses that managed to swim ashore in the gale. Just imagine what the islanders must have thought when they saw animals like those – which they had probably never seen before – rising up out of the waves, in the midst of a raging storm.'

'What happened to the *Juno*?'

'The search for it goes on. We know it's opposite the beach at Tom's Cove – as little as half a mile out to sea, some say. Whoever finds it will become a multi-millionaire, because documents from the period show that when the *Juno* set out from Veracruz bound for Cadiz, its holds contained no less than twenty-two tons of silver.'

'Is that a lot?'

'To give you a rough idea: in 1985, the booty found aboard the galleon *Our Lady of Atocha*, off the Florida coast, by an American called Mel Fisher, was valued at over sixty billion pesetas.'

'Seriously?'

'Deadly seriously. So, who knows, had I stayed on in Central America you might by now be about to inherit a *faaabulous and vast fortune.'*

These words are in italics because Truman said them in a deep melodramatic voice, as though he were the evil character in a film for children. Maceo laughed because that joke always made him laugh, although as usual, he also realised that his grandfather was trying to distract his attention, and that he only added these sorts of comments to his stories in order to make them seem more remote, less sad. In any case, Maceo knew more or less instinctively what Truman's words really meant: some men find everything they look for, while others lose everything they ever had; most of those in the second category dream of joining the first, but never do.

'But then', he said, coming in with another one of his changes of subject, 'you came back to Spain because the lovely Delia had died.'

'Yes. And that was like passing from day to night. You can't even . . . Let's just say that if I had to sum up what I found in one word that word, would be *darkness*. You see, it was like finding yourself at the bottom of a well. The darkness was everywhere: in the shops, in the houses, in people's gazes, in the clothes they wore, in the way they spoke or kept silent. People were no longer themselves.'

'What do you mean, they were no longer themselves?'

'The Civil War had turned them into either victims or victors, which left some people deformed by fear, others by pride. They looked as though . . . as though they were mouldy, I can't think of a better way of putting it. They found themselves wandering about a country of sacristans and Falangists, of common graves and of cemeteries, a country where everything was open to suspicion, all was sinful. Unbelievable though it may sound, nothing was the same as before; words had even taken on horrible new meanings which they never previously had, words like walk, ditch, coffee.'

'Coffee?'

'That was the word the military used when they wanted to order the execution of a prisoner. We know that when General Queipo de Llano received a phone call from Granada asking him what should be done with the poet Federico García Lorca, the answer he gave was: "Coffee, give him plenty of coffee." And don't go thinking I'm revealing any big secret, everyone knows that story by now.'

'But what were people frightened of when you came back to Spain? The war was over.'

'Franco's regime purged large numbers of people, including innocent civilians and unarmed prisoners; that was his idea of peace, I suppose; it's far easier for a criminal to take out a pistol than to put it back in its holster. They say those days were awful – it seemed they would never end. People were shot at dawn, left to die in prisons. Poor wretches. Weren't you made to read Miguel Hernández at school? No? Well, Miguel Hernández was another great poet, just like García Lorca, and he too was captured and left by those bastards to rot in a cell. Anyway, all this came after I had been in Panama and Mexico, and I still haven't told you about that part yet.'

'You were in Panama, working in a furniture shop; but you didn't like it. Cecilia had stayed in Costa Rica. You ate very little and worked very hard – to save money.'

'Yes, that's a good summary. So good, in fact, that it almost doesn't sound like a summary at all – as though there really wasn't much else to tell.'

'And Cecilia's letters.'

'The letters, that's right.'

'And the trip to El Salvador.'

'Of course – the letters. Looking back on it now though, I can see that they caused me a great deal of suffering. It was as if each one made Cecilia more and more of an impossible dream. You see, when you write feelings down they become very formal, somehow less human; they seem to grow gradually cooler and cooler, less recognisable, like a liquid taken off the boil or a figure walking off into the distance. That's how you feel about the letters you receive. As for those you send, for some reason they always contain something to be ashamed of, something either superfluous or lacking, and in both cases it was something important enough for the person who receives them to feel greatly disappointed. It all drives you mad. That's what it does – it drives you mad.'

'But you kept sending them.'

'Ah, but that doesn't mean . . . It's like survivors of a shipwreck having to drink sea water. That, too, can send you out of your mind, they say.' He looked at Maceo, then closed his eyes; on opening them he seemed lost in thought, as though he had just received a piece of disheartening news. It seemed he was about to say something more, but he did not.

'Then you went to El Salvador with Cecilia and you both went down inside the volcano and it was full of orchids.'

'Her father had bought her a car.' Truman was starting to feel tired.

'A Ford. He had bought her a Ford, with white wheels.'

'That's right. He bought it right after I left for Panama, so I suppose it must have been a form of compensation, because that's what men who are powerful usually do: that's for you, and this is for me. In fact the exact opposite happened, because he was unexpectedly called away to Europe on business, and that's when we planned our little trip to El Salvador. I went down to San José and then we crossed Nicaragua. It only lasted ten days. Ten days alone together. We visited the Quezaltepec volcano and the San Miguel, the Cerro Verde, the Izalco.'

'And the waterfalls.'

'Yes, all of that. I remember the last day we spent in the Gulf of Fonseca, not far from the city of La Unión: we were sitting on Tamarindo beach when I told her that the furniture factory owners in Panama had offered to transfer me to Mexico to put me in charge of one of their factories, on triple my old salary. Cecilia encouraged me to accept, saying what difference could it make how far away I went, so long as she remained waiting for me in the same place. Then she started talking about the 'third blue' – which was the sort of thing she liked to invent from time to time. "Look," she said, "over there is the ocean, which is sapphire-blue; and up there is the sky, which is turquoise-blue. *Everyone* knows about them. But then, at this time of the day, and for a few seconds only, just before the sun disappears from view, a ray of light appears on the horizon – see it, that ray the colour of indigo?

That is the third blue, and it's there just for you and me."

'The sweet nothings of lovers, eh? And yet I never did forget it, you know. It's still here.' He said this without an accompanying gesture, so Maceo had no idea whether he was referring to his head or to his heart. 'Even now, after all that has happened, I still think about it every time I look out of the window or go for a walk. It's strange how . . . when you look back on your life . . . it's as if you had dropped, say, a vase, one you really liked; there it is at your feet, smashed into tiny pieces, and yet, as well as the pieces you can also somehow still see the vase intact . . . that's how you'll always remember it. That's the worst word of all – *always*; it's the most . . . the most terrible.'

Truman's eyes closed. Silence descended on the room, one of those silences that seem to exist to allow people to feel alone and to think about death.

'The sun is made of helium and nitrogen,' Maceo said. 'Did you know that?'

But his attempt at prolonging the conversation came to nothing.

He began to make a list in his head of things he liked and those he disliked: falling asleep on the back seat of the car, avoiding jellyfish on a beach, chocolate ice cream, reading in the sun, liver fillets. Then he placed his right hand over Truman's heart: the heartbeats seemed to slip through his fingers, rather like when he tried to drink water from a river. He went over to the chest of drawers on the other side of the room, and searched through their contents: he found Truman's Parker fountain pen and Ronson lighter; the diary from 1956, its pages filled with notes written in moss-green ink in a rather flowery handwriting; his yellow leather gloves from Argentina; his passport with all its customs stamps – Panama's was round, El Salvador's was in the shape of a map, Mexico's was long and narrow with a small circle in the middle showing an eagle killing a snake. He was not searching for anything in particular; he was simply making sure that everything was in its proper place.

He left Truman's room and walked to his parents' bedroom with his eyes closed, pretending to be blind, a boy who had lost his eyesight in an accident – what kind: a plane crash, a car accident? He opened the wardrobe and began searching through the pockets of the coats. He came across the usual items – bus tickets, loose change – then he found something unexpected in Samuel's khaki-coloured duffel coat: a set of keys that weren't the house keys, attached to a copper ring. He wondered where they came from, what they were doing there. He decided to keep a couple of coins as well as the keys, which he stared at for a long while, as if merely by staring long enough he would discover what they opened. On hearing the sound of the front door, he put them away in his pocket and ran to the living room – though first running through the hallway, past the kitchen and, once more, his sister's and parents' bedrooms. He said hello to his mother, who was serving herself a cup of coffee and looked exhausted.

'Did you know that on Venus there are mountains taller than Mount Everest?' he asked her. 'I bet you didn't! And that Mars has deserts and a volcano called Olympus that is twenty-four kilometres high.'

'Good heavens. That's . . . incredible.'

'And a long time ago there was also a gigantic river, which was wider and deeper than the Amazon.'

'Really?'

'It's as true as me being hit by lightning.'

She could still feel the fear, an engrossing, irrational fear of something which she felt certain would not happen to her but which nevertheless, she could not put out of her mind; it lent her the vulnerable, tormented look of those patients who survive major surgery and return to their daily lives of noisy shops and peaceful mornings, only to find their surroundings strangely intimidating. A set of rusty tools, a bucket of empty bottles, a spade, a drawer full of shoes – in everything they detect a warning, a funereal note, for perhaps, in the depths of their eyes, there still lingers a fragment of the horrific darkness they saw and from which many cannot, or for some remote reason will not break free. So profound is the link remaining that on occasion they even feel nostalgia for what they so fear: nostalgia for the hospitals, the chloroform, the insipid food, the scalpels.

Certain aspects of the condition in which Marta found herself struggling – that unease which neither allowed her to sleep nor ever to feel fully awake; it not only made the rest of her life seem non-existent, it even gave her the impression that before then there had, in fact, been nothing, that her past had been futile or empty – brought to mind the terrible growth pains she had suffered as an adolescent. It reminded her of how much she had come to hate her own joints, and the bones that were pierced by the progress of tiny nails, distressed by the invisible hammers and handsaws at work inside. There were times – in the midst of this daily ordeal, which the painkillers, massages, and hot baths administered by Ruth could barely relieve – when Marta imagined herself inside her own body, looking on as her hands grew by a centimetre or her skull slowly expanded. Had she been able to, she would have pulled her limbs up by their roots, so it was strange to think that it was from precisely this unbearable torment that her vocation for medicine would spring. One night, wakeful and tired of suffering without knowing what from, she had begun looking through the volumes of her father's illustrated encyclopaedia to try and identify the cause of her torment; and that was her introduction to the world of kneecaps, femurs, and tibias; she slowly drew her skeleton on a sheet of paper, at first including only the basic parts, before adding those that were more complex: the five segments of the metatarsus in the sole of the foot, the triquetral bone in the wrist, the sphenoid at the base of the cranium, the temporal bone at the side of the skull, the hyoid in between the tongue and the larynx.

'Bones', she was telling Truman, with whom she spoke as much in those days as Maceo would later on; and whom she encouraged to ask her hundreds of questions, 'are essentially deposits of calcium and phosphorus.'

'What are their parts called?'

'The ends are the epiphysis and the bit in the middle is the diaphysis.'

'That's right, diaphysis or marrow,' said her grandfather, glancing down at her notes, which every day contained ever larger and more detailed coloured diagrams and charts. 'How many types are there?'

'Three: long, short, and flat. Long bones have red bone marrow, the others, yellow. And the process by which bones are formed is osteogenesis.'

When she was twenty, the insomnia and the sensation of being torn apart returned, but the big difference between now and then was that this time it was not something whose causes or progress she would find explained in an encyclopaedia, nor did it have anything to do with a vertebrate structure that could be sketched on a sheet of paper – it was an unknown, untraceable ill, which made her feel lost and set her apart, for no distance is greater than the distance between a person and what that person does not know. Her confusion was matched by her fear, for on the one hand, she wanted to live with Lucas and had already found an apartment in an outlying area of the city, while at the same time she was like someone who needed to believe but had no faith in God: someone dying of thirst who suspected the water to be poisoned, and for whom that mere suspicion – whether true or false – was as potent and dangerous as a snakebite.

In her troubled dreams Marta found herself running through a dark world, never knowing what each next step would bring: whether a valley or a ravine, a forest or a precipice, a beach or a cliff. It was there, on glimpsing a movement in the undergrowth, or catching the sound of a flower crushed underfoot – clover, poppies, forget-me-nots, snapdragons – or the hypnotic call of an owl (*hoot*, was that the word she'd been taught at school, she wondered: the dog barks, the frog croaks, the owl hoots) that Marta felt a coldness, an icy coldness, and she realised there was an element of truth in a phrase which until then had always seemed trivial, rhetorical, or absurd, and which she had heard ad nauseam in so many bad films and trashy novels: *her blood froze*, they felt the fear *make their blood freeze*. For that was exactly what she thought she felt as the doubts, and the words that encapsulated those doubts – damage, risk, loneliness – followed her every-where she went, hovered over her heart like vultures over a wounded animal, time and again tracing ever-decreasing circles in the sky.

Back in her bedroom, she decided to look in a different direction, towards all that she would gain by living with Lucas: she would have him, his hands and his eyes, his beautiful naked body – biceps, deltoids, pectorals, serrati – she would have his mornings and his nights; and she would be cutting her ties with her home, with that grim atmosphere in which Maceo and Truman never stopped talking, while everyone else persisted in keeping quiet and ignoring one another, their stubbornness thereby forming a pointless space, a wasteland where nothing would grow, as always happens when one silence is added to another.

At times, during these nights without end, exhausted by hours of discomfort which failed to bring sleep and only left her feeling all the more awake, Marta would sit up in bed, grumbling like a woman twice her weight, and listen to tapes through her earphones or go into the living room to read the newspaper: an American woman called Janet Ray told the story of how she had recovered the body of her father, a pilot shot down over the Bay of Pigs in 1961 and whose embalmed corpse Fidel Castro had kept in a freezer for almost twenty years as proof that the attempted invasion of Cuba had originated in America; every time the enemies of the revolution denied their involvement in the matter, Castro threatened to exhibit his terrifying piece of evidence on a table at the United Nations.

She flicked through the paper: international news, sport, society, culture. She felt faint from exhaustion and so much continued suspicion. She went into the kitchen and looked for something to eat in the refrigerator. There was something pleasant about the family fridge, its well-stocked shelves, the way Samuel had meticulously arranged items according to their use-by date and condition: top shelf or at the front for food that most urgently needed to be consumed or was the most perishable – mince, chicken, fresh milk; lower shelves for cans, yogurts, and other items; vegetable compartment for cold cuts and fruit. Marta sat down to eat a piece of chocolate. In November 1970 the authorities of the German Democratic Republic had exhumed the body of Goethe from the Princes' Crypt and transported it in a van through the streets of Weimar, to a laboratory where it was to be mummified before going on display to the public, the same as the Russians had done with Lenin in Moscow.

She closed the newspaper. In her last year of studying literature at school, before opting for sciences, she had had to read *The Sorrows of Young Werther* for an exam. She remembered the novel, but most of all she remembered – why? – an aphorism of Goethe's, which her teacher had written up on the blackboard one afternoon: 'Even rubbish shines when the sun comes out.'

'At times, things don't have a meaning,' she told herself angrily, as if to rebut an accusation, 'however much you can't forget them. Right now, I have in my mind that photograph of the pilot they shot down over Cuba, and his life story: he held the rank of captain, was born in Alabama, his name was Thomas though everyone called him Pete, he looked like Glenn Ford. I may even remember him for a long time to come – but what difference does that make.'

She hoped that this time, Lucas would like the apartment she had found. The first had been much nicer and in a better area, but when she took him to see it her plans had collapsed in a matter of seconds. She broke off another ounce of chocolate and then closed her eyes so that Lucas would ring at the door of that small apartment again, just as he had a week before. At the sound of the bell, she ran to plug in a cassette-player ready with a tape of songs he liked and took out a couple of cans of beer she had left to chill in the fridge.

'Welcome,' she said, handing him a beer. 'Welcome to our home.'

Lucas stood in the doorway, a smile curling his lips – his usual smug, half-hearted smile. That smile which Marta so adored.

'Your home, darling. Yours, not mine. At the moment I'm broke, you know that.'

'Fine. That's the best part about starting from nothing: from now on things can only get better.'

Marta closed the door. They kissed. And, as she let him fondle her breasts, she glimpsed the domestic bliss she so dreamed of.

'It's harder when it's uphill all the way,' Lucas suddenly said, breaking off their embrace. 'Anyway, I'm not so sure about this. Maybe this isn't such a good idea.'

'What isn't? What is it you want . . . what's . . .' She could have slapped herself: whatever happened to all her biting wit and clever small talk every time she found herself alone with Lucas? Why the sudden paralysis, the cretinous stuttering? 'Well . . . come on, then!' She rubbed her hands in the manner of an unctuous seminarist or obsequious shop assistant, neither of which was her usual style: 'No reason to stand around chatting, let's finish these beers and visit Manderley.' Lucas seemed not to get the joke, or not to find it funny '. . . You know – Daphne du Maurier, *Rebecca* and all that,' she added.

They drank their beers in silence, staring round at the empty apartment, noting the impersonal white walls and small windows; Lucas still wearing the same sour, pitying expression that was so typical of him and which his enemies so hated and his followers so revered; and she unable to look him in the eye, all of a sudden feeling weak and drained, aware that her hands had begun to tremble violently. To make matters worse, it seemed that the songs on the tape – Portishead, Massive Attack, 4 hero; the kind of music that Iraide said sounded like 'a cross between some poseurs, some tasteless food and Barry White' – served only to make the situation all the more unnatural and uncomfortable. The magic she had glimpsed earlier was already vanishing for good, to be replaced, in her case, by old anxieties and nerves – just as when the sun comes out, the snow melts and again lays bare the dirty everyday pavements, worn asphalt, and ordinary buildings that were there before.

'Right. Let's go!' she said, trying to sound jovial, relaxed – the tone of voice many use when speaking with children, or adults whom they fear. 'Before you say anything, come and see the other rooms' – though she knew that it was not the rent Lucas was unsure of, it was her. 'Here we have a nice quiet room, which you could use for studying; this is the bedroom, with its own little balcony; and this is the kitchen, of course we'd need to get a dishwasher, maybe also an oven.'

'Hey, this is Massive Attack,' Lucas said. 'I love this band, and that great Bristol groove.'

'Well, erm . . . *c'est tout*, as the French would say. That's it. All we need to do now is decide what I do with the money.' Marta took from her bag the cheque for the deposit and first two months' rent. It represented her savings, a loan from Iraide – whom she intended to repay as

144

soon as she received her first pay cheque – plus the thirty thousand pesetas she got for her compact disc collection in one of the dingy second-hand shops off the Gran Vía.

'It's just that . . . look, there's something I don't understand,' Lucas said. 'You go to all this effort' – he caressed her shoulder, then her neck – 'and I, well, like I said, I can't even afford to get my motorbike fixed. The garage sent me a bill . . . Nothing's gone right ever since my parents got divorced. And how would I get here from university? By *metro*?' He made it sound as though the metro were a repulsive place, teeming with sick, greasy people. 'I'm broke at the moment. Maybe in the future, when things sort themselves out; or if I could somehow get my bike back. You know how much I like . . .' – he undid a button of her shirt – '. . . being with you.'

Marta did not want to put him under any pressure, but she could feel the anxiety returning: he's leaving my God he's slipping through my fingers what can I do my God he's leaving me what can I do oh my God oh my God.

'OK,' she said, 'well, if you want, we'll leave it until things . . .' Lucas stayed right where he was, impassive, not saying a word. 'And I suppose you could pay off the money you owe on your bike with . . . well, if I gave you this cheque.'

For a few seconds the expression in Lucas's eyes seemed to change, to undergo a sudden shock: it became the gaze of a man seeing a train rattle by; the gaze of a man about to fire a shot. Then, he started stroking Marta's neck again, undid a second button of her shirt.

'What are you talking about? You're not saying you want to give me your money, are you? And you think I'd accept? Well, that's certainly a surprise – I don't know if I should feel flattered or offended. But, hey, thanks anyway.

You know you're so . . .' – he opened up the front of her blouse, began caressing her breasts – '. . . so generous, and so pretty. Did you really mean what you said?'

Marta picked up the cheque again and somewhat solemnly placed it in the pocket of Lucas's jacket.

'Of course I did,' she replied. 'I really meant it.' She stepped back to slip her blouse off; she undid her bra and removed her skirt, then knelt in front of Lucas, pulled down the zip of his trousers. 'And I really mean this too.'

Two days later, Lucas came to collect her from the secretarial college on his Vespa, and as they crossed the city – caught up in a tide of wing mirrors, flashing tail lights, headlamps, and car stickers: a tiger, a bulls-eye, one that read 'Get in or get back' – Marta was once more able to clearly make out the contours of the life she so desired.

This mirage soon vanished, however; the oasis turned rapidly back to sand. Heaps of hot, lonely sand. One evening, puzzled, and worried again, this time because Lucas had not come to fetch her, either that afternoon or the day before; no longer able to bear the prickling spread of jealousy, she decided to phone his home.

'Hello?' It was the voice of his mother.

'Could I speak to Lucas, please?'

'Lucas? He's not here. But I thought . . . just a moment.' Marta heard her put a hand over the mouthpiece and whisper to someone: 'Stop it, behave yourself.'

'Hello? Sorry about that. *Turn the volume down, will you.* I thought he was with you. He said . . . excuse me again, just a second. *What's got into you . . . ha ha ha . . . don't be so impatient.* Hello, Luisa? I thought you were both off to the house in the woods for another one of those parties. Can you hear me? Hello? *Damn. Now see what you've done? She must have put the phone down, because of you.* Luisa?'

146

Sitting in the kitchen of her parents' apartment, Marta tried once more to piece together the parts of the jigsaw. Had Lucas taken Luisa to the house up in the mountains or was it just that his mother had got the names mixed up? Had he really used her money to get his bike repaired or had it never needed repairing in the first place? In which case all she had done was provide him with the funds to go off and enjoy himself with another woman. She wondered why Lucas had never mentioned the cheque again. Had she been right not to ask him about it or should she have demanded an explanation? She had held back, hoping that the innocence and nobility she found so hard to feign would at least not pass unnoticed; but even as she suffered in silence, she recalled a maxim that Samuel – who was never less than sententious and grandiloquent – used to lecture her with: 'Innocence will lead you into a thousand tight spots, but it won't get you out of a single one.' I hope he's wrong, she thought to herself.

The next morning, a Saturday, she was taking Lucas to see the second apartment, the one near the outskirts of the city. But even if it was to his liking, they wouldn't be able to take it until she received her salary from the clinic, where she had been working for only two weeks. In the afternoons, at the Faculty, she was studying harder than ever before, because when she became a doctor, in two or three years' time, it would all be much easier: she'd set up her own practice, make a name for herself, have more patients than she needed. And Lucas would always be there, in the other wing of an apartment in Calle Serrano, or Calle Jorge Juan, perhaps Calle Felipe II near where it crossed Calle Goya, or maybe even the smarter section of the Paseo de la Castellana – one of those large apartments with small balconies and high ceilings, the kind of place where you could build up a world of comfort and stability. When she felt like being with him, she'd do what she did right now: she pushed the red button on the intercom and told a secretary – Inés? Paz? Fátima? – to kindly ask the next patient to wait; then she slipped out of a back door, the one behind the desk, and went along to the office where Lucas wasn't expecting her.

'Darling! What are you doing here?'

'What do you think I'm going to do?' said Marta, who was now far bolder and more confident than at the time she imagined this very episode, six or seven years earlier.

On her way back along the corridor to her consulting room she remembered what was, according to her old friend Iraide, who was still as clever and cynical as ever, a guaranteed recipe for a happy and stable marriage: one day a week you do everything he wants, and for the other six you'll be free to do whatever you like.

Amid all this fantasising, Marta noticed that she was at last feeling sleepy. She put the chocolate back where she had found it, returned to her room and lay down on the bed. From the adjacent bedroom came the sound of Samuel coughing heavily: larynx, epiglottis, trachea, she thought to herself. She had to convince him to get that seen to. Though with him everything was always so complicated, and any matter, however trivial, always required so much beating about the bush, so much debate.

A thick, misty silence was descending over her, blocking out the outside world, save for one last car, save for the sound of her father again, that booming noise that now already reached her from a long way off – oesophagus, bronchial tree, lungs . . . And all of a sudden she found herself in the same forest as before. That same unknown, murky forest. What was she doing there? What was she

148

looking for? Or were others looking for her? She wondered where Lucas was.

'Hey!' she shouted. 'Lucas! It's not funny . . . Lu-*caaaas*!'

She looked up at the darkened sky. Then she walked on until she glimpsed a light in the distance, amid the trees: it was a van, parked on a forest path; inside was a man, and he too was gazing attentively up at the night sky. She may well wonder about the van, the next morning – if she still remembered any of this, that is – for instance whether it was blue or yellow; but it would be in vain, for you never know what colour things are in dreams. She told herself to try at least to remember how the section of pine forest picked out by the headlamps differed from the rest: the enamelled earth, the circle of phosphorescent grass. She stepped up a little closer to the man behind the wheel.

'There are many different types of eagles,' the man said, still gazing stubbornly upwards. 'The fishing eagle, which lives close to rivers, eats fishes and ducks; the golden eagle, which nests in the mountains and hunts down in the valleys for deer, foxes, and squirrels; the imperial eagle likes steppes and marshland, and feeds on hares and rabbits; the Bonelli eagle is to be found in rocky habitats and lives off lizards; the booted eagle prefers hills, only ever perches on evergreen trees, and lives off quails and insects. And that's without even mentioning the goshawk, the sparrowhawks, the falcons, the . . .'

Marta ran off; she scrambled down a small slope and kept on running until she reached the bank of a stream and, further on, came to a small estuary. There she sat down, leaning back against the trunk of a black poplar.

'Lucas,' she said aloud. 'I bet that if I stay here nice and quietly, sooner or later he'll come and find me.'

CHAPTER FIVE

He must have left home about half an hour earlier but had forgotten why – which meant he now found himself in a truly bizarre and awkward situation, a sort of insoluble chaos, a blind alley. Was he by any chance losing his mind? He felt again in the pockets of his jacket, trousers, and duffel coat, but could find no clue or detail to remind him why he had stepped out. Then he considered other factors, for example, the amount of money he had in his wallet, the direction he was heading in when he realised he had no idea where he was going, but these too revealed little: he was four or five hundred metres from home and was holding a small package wrapped in grey greaseproof paper of the kind used by butchers, so he supposed that was the reason he had left the apartment – to go and buy something for supper, though of course there was no way to be certain. In any case there was more to it than that. Why had he walked off down the street afterwards, instead of going straight home with the food? The questions infuriated him, made him feel as obtuse and helpless as one of those little children who sit for hours in front of a flower, waiting for it to grow, convinced that merely by staring long enough they will suddenly be able to see the petals or calyx expand, or a leaf or the stalk extend by a millimetre. That was just how Samuel felt in that moment.

He leant on the bar in the hospital cafeteria and asked the waiter for another beer. He was almost the only customer, except for three or four others who sat there staring down into their cups or glasses as though their misfortunes were to be found dissolved in those hot or tepid, carbonated or still, sweet or bitter liquids; as though therein lay the explanation for all that was happening to them. Leaving thoughts of these people aside, Samuel began to make a mental list of items, other than the meat for the supper, which he or his family might have needed: vegetables, toothpaste, a loaf of bread, biscuits, salt, washing powder; some oil for the hinges of the door to the study, a new light bulb for the larder. But no, Samuel knew that it was none of these. What he actually suspected was that it had something to do with the missing keys, though he did not know how or to what extent. Where were they? When did he lose them? Had someone taken them from their hiding place in his duffel coat? Who could it have been, and why? How would he ever get to the bottom of all this without first having to explain where the keys came from and about the incident with the woman he had followed?

He paid and left, keeping the change. On seeing the worn, slightly damp banknote he'd been given, he began imagining its possible history, how it had passed from hand to hand, changing owner and district, losing its stiffness, turning from a crunchy to a pale green. The waiter had received it, Samuel decided, from a woman whose father had just died in the hospital; she was still in a state of lethargy, a state that verged on indifference, and consisted of grief but also of relief: what could we have done, there was no cure for him, he was making all our lives a misery, at least his suffering's over now. The man remained on a separate floor of the building, until orderlies came to take him away; his daughter ordered a tea, a sandwich, another tea; the man the deceased had shared the room with was watching a tennis match on television, trying to forget that alongside him, in the next bed, lay a corpse under a sheet.

The woman had been given the note by a taxi driver who'd had too much to drink, and he, in turn, had been given it by a doctor whose wife was unfaithful. That same night, almost at dawn, the taxi driver would have an accident, after which all the previous evening's events would strike him as unusual occurrences – steps clearly leading up to the accident: the fact that he had drunk two glasses of wine with his meal, not one; the fact that he had smoked two more cigarettes than normal; that he had had an argument with a female passenger. The doctor thought about how he wouldn't have minded owning a gun.

Samuel would have liked to find an ending for the story, some device to give the narrative unity and meaning. But he could not, for from the moment he set eyes on him, he was unable to get that last man out of his head, that doctor who knew – how did he know? what irrefutable evidence did he have? – that his wife was unfaithful.

He was still thinking about this man as he entered a supermarket to buy some oil, a litre of real olive oil in a glass bottle; the soya oil which Ruth used disagreed with him, it seemed to burn the lining of his stomach; it may even have been the cause of all that dizziness and the coughing fits he had had for some time now and whose causes he ignored.

What sort of life did the doctor with the unfaithful wife lead? What mistakes had they themselves made to set them on course for disaster – just as certainly as the taxi driver's own actions, at least in Samuel's opinion, had led to his accident? How hard had they each had to pull from their respective sides before the bonds of marriage had broken? In truth, Samuel had to admit that he had never once envisaged the possibility that Ruth could have done that to him.

155

Or to be more precise, he no longer envisaged it now, for back in the days when they were going out together the situation had been very different. Samuel clearly remembered the thick cobweb of suffering and doubt that had descended over him on more than one occasion; how he had been tormented by the thought that Ruth might leave him or that she was seeing other men behind his back. Indeed, in those days he had done things she never found out about: from spying on her home with a pair of binoculars to searching her bag and, on several occasions, following her in the street when she came out of lectures. He loved her so much that he was ready to die for her, without a moment's hesitation, like in that recurring, masochistic fantasy of his in which he was given the choice: 'Her life or yours.' Samuel, noble and magnanimous to the end, without once looking back, would start walking towards the firing squad, or towards the noose dangling from the tree – the episode invariably took place in wartime, with the country in enemy hands, the Royal Palace in flames – all the while imagining Ruth as she watched him from a lorry or the window of a train drawing away from the scene of the execution.

Unfortunately, life rarely affords us opportunities to show our greatness, usually only our pettiness, as Samuel knew full well; he knew how in the end, egotism and indifference always win over self-sacrifice and loyalty; how the highest aims are soon forgotten in favour of the most shameful forms of servitude. The world should never have been created by God, but by Alexandre Dumas.

Looking into his past, he could see no link that had broken the chain, only a sort of omnipresent border that divided his life into two large regions: heaven and hell. He summarised it thus: Ruth and he had been very happy, then they had become wretched. Why? For a start, Ruth

156

had turned into a different person: she stopped being optimistic and open-minded and became severe and negative instead. The difference between who she once was and who she was now was not hard to see, he told himself: 'Simply swap *conciliatory* with *strict*, *sweet* with *sour*, *easygoing* with *intransigent*, and see how all that these words implied – the shouting, the enmity, the quarrelling – gradually spread over our lives like mould on rotten fruit.' And as he supported this theory with specific images and again heard Ruth calling him a failure, an impostor, an egomaniac or a liar, he sensed his resentment incubate its venom inside him once more; he began to think up cutting remarks and deadly ripostes, irrefutable arguments and rhetorical traps; in short, he started behaving yet again like those men who stop feeding their dogs a night or two before the hunt, in order that they rush and pounce all the more ferociously on the game that is brought down.

But then he stopped himself, for that was the path he never again wanted to tread. That was precisely the direction he should not have been looking in. 'There's nothing there,' he told himself. 'You'll find nothing there.' He was on a bus when he said this, on the way to where he had followed the second woman and been beaten by the men who came to her rescue. Why? What was he after? It was a deep personal need, he supposed, perhaps an urge connected with the loss of the keys or the pure and simple desire to taste the excitement he now felt as he approached the scene of the incident.

He got off at the same stop he used for work and headed in the direction of the park and the deserted area he had been to before. He passed the steelworks, the plots of land. He sensed danger lurking around every corner. What would happen, he wondered, if he came across the blonde woman in the green coat who had taken fright, and run off with short steps, dropping her keys.

Then he returned to the subject of Ruth. Could she have been unfaithful? 'No,' he told himself, 'she's not that kind of woman. What kind of woman? Well, you know what I mean . . . No, I don't know; all women can be *that kind of woman*, if they want to be. The same goes for you when no one's looking. The same as anyone. None of us is just one person.'

He found himself alone in the same spot where he had been knocked around by the men; this time, however, Samuel managed to struggle free, he threw a right hook to the first man's jaw, drove his fist into the second man's stomach, and proceeded to give them a good beating until they ran off.

For a few minutes he stood there panting as if a scuffle really had taken place, still not knowing why he had returned or what he hoped would happen next. Then he walked on until he came to an area where the city seemed to peter out, where the roads and buildings gave way to open land and four or five small houses dotted about a parched field, at the end of which he saw what looked like a small lake with reed beds around its edges. He headed over towards one of the houses, the one with no lights on in the windows. In the dry grass his footsteps sounded as if they were crunching insects and he shuddered at the thought of what might be hiding there: rats, beetles, worms. He sat down on the low wall that skirted the house, which was obviously uninhabited. A short distance away, playing among the trees, he caught sight of a pair of stray cats. He called out 'Here, puss-puss-puss,' rubbing the pad of his thumb against his index finger, but the cats remained where they were.

Then he thought of Ruth, and again heard her calling

him an impostor, a failure. Is that what she thought of him? He tried to take stock of his own lost hopes, of the men he had once dreamt of becoming: he was going to be an engineer, a teacher, a scientist. Or maybe have a career in politics. But something had happened to each of them – the engineer died young, without building a single bridge, the victim of Samuel's material needs; the teacher and the eminent scientist both lost faith in themselves, before teaching anything or making any new discoveries; the political leader was betrayed. 'I never became any of those men,' Samuel muttered, beginning one of his monologues, 'and I can assure you that I have no regrets. If I had, right now I'd be somewhere else entirely, doing something completely different.'

Maybe Ruth too was thinking about all this? Did she feel let down? She did, that much was clear, but to what extent? Let down enough to be unfaithful? He remembered the packet of meat and the bottle of olive oil in the pockets of his coat. But what if they moved apartment or took a trip to, say, Brazil? A new life, in order to find their old selves.

He unwrapped the meat and set it down on the ground, on the other side of the wall, so that it would attract the cats. It was decided, then, that's what they'd do: new home, new neighbourhood, Brazil, Rio de Janeiro. Maybe they'd go dancing on the Copacabana. It was the sort of thing Ruth used to like.

He slipped his hand into his other pocket, but did so very slowly so as not to frighten off the cats, who were right at his feet now, making a repulsive sound as they chewed.

Ruth? Ruth with someone else? Telling him yes, yes, go on, or fuck me, fuck me, fuck me, you bastard, fuck me, fuck me, fuck me, fuck me, like some actress in a porn film?

He grasped the neck of the bottle, gripping it so hard that his fingers hurt. He'd call in at a travel agency the very next day, start making arrangements that would lead to Brazil, samba, Astrud Gilberto, Ipanema Beach. Or maybe an even better idea might be Samoa: the light of the tropics, the coral reefs, the tomb of Robert Louis Stevenson. 'Did you know that as a mark of friendship,' Ruth told him from 1981, in New York, 'any one of the island's inhabitants is allowed to give you his or her name? Afterwards they call a big meeting where everyone helps to pick a new one.'

Maybe that was what they needed – not to find anything new but to get something back, to return to the beginning so as to put off the end. And why not? After all, he had some savings set aside, in a special account he'd never mentioned to Ruth.

The sound of the word *Samoa* brought to mind an image of Ruth naked, the way the taste of honey can sometimes recall the buzzing of bees. What had happened to the two of them? Just how disappointed was she? Was her disappointment great enough to lead her to another man's bed? He brought the bottle down hard on one of the cats, the grey one, knocking the animal to the ground, where its paws went on moving spasmodically. He struck again, this time even harder, and again, breaking the bottle. The olive oil spilled everywhere – soya oil for dinner again, then; not that it tasted so bad, and besides, it was certainly cheap. He stared down at the dead animal. Already it looked nothing like a cat, or anything else for that matter; more like some shapeless being, something from another planet. He turned and began his journey home. He felt fine; a little agitated but otherwise fine. Tomorrow he'd drop by the travel agency. Or the day after – perhaps it was best to give himself a break, and leave things for a couple of days.

'So that one up there must be Perseus,' Truman said. 'Which means the one on the right has to be Andromeda and the one beyond that Pegasus. Above them is Cassiopeia. And a little further south, the Whale. How wonderful it is to see history written up there like that.'

Sitting side by side on the terrace that had been struck by the lightning, Maceo and his grandfather were trying to spot the constellations and galaxies shown in one of Maceo's illustrated books. They had the same binoculars as on the night of the comet and were talking in whispers, like a pair of generals discussing the course of a battle.

'What history?'

'Those are all names of Greek gods. Most star formations are named after Greek or Roman gods. Do you know what mythology is?'

'A bit. Hercules and Zeus, right? Achilles and his heel, the Trojan horse.'

'Well, Perseus was the son of Danae and Jupiter, who had seduced her by becoming a shower of golden rain and entering the tower in which she'd been locked up. When he was older, Perseus was ordered to kill the gorgon Medusa, who lived on the edge of the world and had snakes instead of hair. Anyone who looked at her was immediately turned to stone.'

'She turned people into statues? For ever?'

'That's right.'

'So she was very powerful.'

'Yes, I think she must have been. Just as well they gave him weapons that could defeat her.'

'Who did? What weapons?'

'Let's see now . . .' Truman rubbed his chin with his thumb and squinted with his left eye, '. . . only yesterday I was . . . Let's see if I remember: the nymphs gave him Pluto's helmet, to render him invisible; Minerva gave him a mirror, Vulcan a scythe, and I think Mercury gave him a sack. With all that help, he was able to cut her head off, and from the blood of her neck was born Pegasus, the winged horse, the son of Neptune. Anyway, this is all just to say that that star up there – see it, in the lower part of the constellation? – is called Algol, which means "the head of the ogre", because that's supposed to be where Medusa's head would have been while Perseus was holding it.'

The boy swung his binoculars to where Truman was pointing and then looked back down at the map of the night sky in his book. He liked Truman's stories so much that he always rushed to hear them with a kind of blind belief, so excited was he by what he might discover – like the person walking down the street who steps into a small crowd of onlookers, without knowing what they have gathered to see: a conjuror, a con man, or a corpse.

'What about the other constellations?'

'Andromeda was the daughter of Cassiopeia and the wife of Perseus. What happened to them was that Neptune decided to punish Cassiopeia, who was queen of Ethiopia, for having declared her own daughter to be more beautiful than the Nereids.'

'Who were the Nereids?'

'They were a kind of siren who protected sailors during storms. And so Neptune unleashed a great flood over the country and sent a sea monster to destroy it.'

'What monster?'

'A whale. And then King Cepheus . . .'

'. . . Cassiopeia's husband.'

'Correct. Well done. As I was saying, King Cepheus then consulted the oracle of Ammon.'

'Who was Ammon? What's an oracle?'

Truman wiped a handkerchief over his forehead.

'Yes, well . . . Ammon was the most powerful of the Egyptian Gods, and the oracle was a place where the future was predicted. There, King Cepheus learnt that his kingdom would survive the disaster only if he sacrificed his daughter; so he chained Andromeda to a stone and left her there to be devoured by the monster. But Perseus was prepared to kill so that he could marry the princess.'

'He killed the king?'

'No, not the king – the whale!'

'Ah, yes of course – the whale!' said Maceo with a certain affectation, already using the words and gestures of one of the men he might one day have become, but whom he now eliminated once and for all from his list of options – there and then, on realising just how ridiculous and superficial he sounded in that role, as if feeling in advance some of the put-downs or shaming sarcasm that others would hold in store, those twists of the knife that people reserve for those they consider too smug or frivolous.

Maceo swung the binoculars back to the stars, which now seemed more familiar.

'How wonderful to think', Truman said, glancing alternately between the book and the sky, 'that they're up there and that they all have these beautiful names: the Hydra, the Bird of Paradise, the Magellanic Clouds, the Southern Cross.'

'I wish we could always stay together,' Maceo said. 'I wish you didn't have to go.'

'What?'

'No . . . what I mean is . . .'

'No, no, don't worry. There's nothing wrong with thinking about that. After all, it's only biology, the passage of time . . . and I suppose that looking into space makes you realise what little you have. Did you know that time has changed a lot, and that it wasn't always the same? I've been reading a lot about that recently.'

'What do you mean, time wasn't always the same?'

'The Egyptian calendar comprised twelve months of thirty days each – in other words, a total of 360 days – plus another five that weren't part of any month. The Romans only had ten months, which is why our year ends September, October, November, December, all of which take their names from the Latin words for seven, eight, nine, and ten. It was the Emperor Julius Caesar who added the other two we have now. So you see what I mean?'

'*Nov*ember – nine. *Dec*ember – ten.'

'But the leap years caused so much confusion that Pope Gregory XIII instituted some drastic changes, and so . . . Pass me that book, I just want to . . . And so in 1542 the fourth of October was followed not by the fifth of October, but by the fifteenth.'

'Like when the clocks go forward in spring and at two o'clock in the morning you have to move the time to three.'

'Exactly. By coincidence Saint Teresa of Ávila died on that very same fourth of October and was buried the following morning, eleven days later.'

'Really?'

'That's what happened.'

'Why do you know all these things?'

'I'm not sure. I'm not even sure of what use they are to anyone, though I still think it's better to know them than not.'

'And we follow Julius Caesar's calendar?'

'No, because other changes were made: one by Mark Antony, who changed the month of *quintillis* to July, in honour of the Emperor Julius. Another by the Emperor Augustus, who gave his name to what used to be the sixth month, *sixtillis*, and added an extra day so that it would have as many as Julius Caesar's month. But we still calculate the year in accordance with the reforms made by Pope Gregory. Mind you, the Christian era also has its ghost year.'

'A year that doesn't exist?'

'Yes, because when Dionysius Exiguus instituted his calendar . . .'

'Was Dionysius Exiguus also a pope?'

'No, he was . . . I don't know, he was the person who had the job of bringing in the new calendar, which basically meant starting the years off from the birth of Christ.'

'I see. That's why we have BC and AD.'

'But the thing is, at the time he was making his calculations, the number zero had yet to be invented, so he had to pass from the year before Jesus was born straight on to the year after Jesus was born.'

'So?'

'Which means the year 100 belonged to the first century, not the second, and that the year 2000 will still be part of the twentieth century – otherwise, the centuries would each only have ninety-nine years, instead of a hundred. But that's not what I wanted to tell you. All I want you to understand is that time is not an exact science. You may think it is, but it isn't. Right now, many people in Japan still count years from the start of the reign of the Emperor. And so what for us will be the year 2000, they will call the year 11 of Akihito . . . In any case, according to some classical writers, it was Mercury who first had the idea of measuring time.'

Maceo wondered if he would be able to remember everything: Julius Caesar and Pope Gregory XIII, the Nereids and the King of Ethiopia, Dionysius Exiguus and Mercury, Andromeda and Perseus . . .

'Did you already know all this when you lived in Central America?'

'Some of it, because Cecilia liked looking at the stars and telling me their names.'

'Altair and Naos,' Maceo interrupted him, 'Vega, Sirius, Antares.'

'. . . or seeing if we could spot the Toucan, the Flying Fish, the Bears . . . When I went to Mexico I was thinking about her so much that I started reading books on astronomy, as well as the classics – Ovid's *Metamorphoses*, Homer's *Iliad* and *Odyssey*, Virgil's *Aeneid*. I spent my evenings in a library in Calle del Correo Mayor or the one in the Palace of Fine Arts. And that was when I made the other great discovery of my life, one that made a huge impression on me – namely that the more I learnt, the more I needed to know. After finishing work at the furniture shop, which was in Paseo de la Reforma, I would go by the second-hand bookshops in Avenida Hidalgo, and after that I'd go to Plaza Dinamarca to read at the base of the statue of George Washington and then . . . '

'Why *second-hand* bookshops?'

'Because as well as second-hand books, they also sold new books at reduced prices. You could pick up some very interesting bargains there. Anyway, soon afterwards, I applied to study philology at the university – I could do that because I had already graduated from high school in Spain. I completed the first two years with very good grades, especially in Latin and Greek. I attended classes in the evenings, and at work I would sit there dreaming about the university professor I'd one day become, about the home that would be mine; I had a vision of Cecilia and our children sitting around the hearth, playing on a swing in the garden. It was a beautiful large house in Coyoacán, close to residences which had once belonged to conquistadors such as Hernán Cortés, Pedro de Alvarado, and Diego de Ordaz.'

'When did you sleep?'

'That wasn't a problem – the classes didn't finish late and I was good at organising myself. There were even days when I found time to drop by the cafés where all the Spaniards used to meet. One was in Calle Bucareli, another was in Calle Santa María la Redonda, another in Calle San Juan de Letrán. I came across some of the exiled poets there on a few occasions – Manuel Altolaguirre, Juan Rejano, Emilio Prados. They loved to spend hours talking, boasting about how, instead of buying furniture for their homes, they had bought new suitcases because Franco wouldn't be around for much longer, because they'd soon be going back to Spain, because the democratic nations of Europe would never allow . . . and so on and so on and so on. Most of them never came back, and are buried in Mexico: León Felipe, Luis Cernuda . . . The Civil War was awful, it left wounds that would never heal, turned people into vermin. I met a woman whose son was executed not far from here, in Las Rozas, by a group of anarchists who hated that rich kid for not letting them enter his game reserve and who took advantage of all the turmoil to murder him; they came for him at dawn, in a lorry; they tied him up hand and foot and dragged him off in front of his mother; several kilometres away they shot him four times in a ditch. Someone – don't ask me who or why – took a photograph of the dead body which his mother kept with her at all times, ready to show to anyone who wanted to see it: "That's my boy," she'd say, "this is what those criminals did to my boy." There is no limit to pain. There is to happiness, but not pain. I hope you never ever have to live through something like that.'

'Were you still writing to Cecilia?'

'I think it was then that I felt closer to her than ever before, because for the first time in my life everything seemed so possible: to work and earn money, to finish my studies, to make something of myself. This was 1948, I had spent ten years in Central America: just over six in Costa Rica, a year in Panama, and the rest in Mexico. I loved Mexico, I loved going for walks in Chapultepec Park or around the Plaza del Zócalo, taking trips to Puebla, to Tacuba, climbing the Popocatépetl volcano . . . Just saying the names brings it all back so clearly . . . And the people – I love the Mexicans, they've got that politeness and yet a gruffness about them too, as if they could fly off the handle at any moment. But if you're respectful towards them, they'll be considerate towards you. You could spend hours just listening to them talking.' He closed his eyes, as though he really could hear that sweet-sounding language and its unusual accent. Maceo guessed that his grandfather was once again about to fall asleep.

'Didn't you go to the Yucatán? That's where the meteorite that killed all the dinosaurs landed. It was ten kilometres wide.'

'No, I didn't. Though I'd have liked to have seen the

Maya cities of Uxmal and Chichén Itzá. The entire coast-line apparently is full of caves and huge natural wells called *cenotes*. They must be wonderful, with trees grow-ing out of the water. Which may have something to do with that meteorite. Anyway, that's another of the things I never did.'

'Because when Delia died it all came to an end?'

Truman glanced up at him, somewhat surprised. His gaze had turned bitter from looking back at beautiful things which were now lost; as bitter as the water in a vase that had contained cut flowers.

'Yes,' he said, 'that's right. Hopes . . . it's best never to take anything for granted.'

'When you came back to Spain did you still look at the stars? Did you go on with your studies?'

'There was neither the time nor place for that kind of thing here. The realities of daily life always got in the way, there was no avoiding them. At first I tried to pull myself together, turn my back on that dull, grey existence. I thought I'd soon be able to sort things out; but I was deluding myself, it was all just a sham and . . . it wears you down, you know: the longer you keep the pretence up, the weaker and less capable you become; when you lose your dreams you're left with yourself, and nothing in this world can take you away from that.'

Truman's face grew sad as he recalled how in Spain his hopes had vanished, taking his identity with them, the way a river loses its name when it flows out into an ocean or sea – it ceases to be the Turia or the Ebro and becomes the Mediterranean; it ceases to be the Miño or the Douro and becomes simply the Atlantic.

'What happened after that?'

'Not much. Time passed, the embers cooled, I grew up

so fast I hardly noticed. I reached that odd point when you're no longer young and yet you're still not old. You become a kind of centaur: half the person you used to be, half somebody else; that point when there's more and more you don't care about and less and less you do . . . You're in no-man's land; you keep moving, but not because you'll get anywhere. And then it gets slowly worse, with each passing year, with each next decade. Have you noticed how people get sad when they look at old photographs? That's because it's unbearable to see what you once were, to see how everything wastes away and that as you get older . . . You don't change, you become deformed.'

Maceo thought Truman was turning back into that man he didn't understand.

'What happened to Cecilia? Didn't you write to her any more?'

'Why? What for? I was at the bottom of a well from which there was no escape, looking after my father who was sick and depressed. Other people treated us as if we had the plague or as though we were inferior beings; in their eyes we were either to be pitied or despised. Do you understand? They were the masters and we were their dogs.'

'When did you come to Madrid?'

'Very soon afterwards; my father had got rheumatism from working on the fish market, and the damp climate in La Coruña wasn't good for him. Here, I found work as an assistant in a grocery. I gave up my studies. I never again went back to looking at the night sky. I never again wrote to Cecilia. What was the point? What can you offer others when you've given up on yourself? Later on I bought the shop with the money I'd saved in Panama and Mexico. I married your grandmother, Aitana, a decent and pretty woman. I can't complain, I don't think that would be fair.'

'What do you mean, "the embers cooled"? That you forgot about Cecilia? That a time came when you stopped thinking about her?'

'If only I could have, but I couldn't. Never. And you know what that means? It means that she was always here' – Truman placed his hand on his heart – 'and although her name never passed my lips again, she stayed there for every second of my life, getting bigger and bigger. It was absurd, but I kept asking myself the same question: "What is she doing now?" I'd ask myself this on the bus; walking up a flight of stairs in a hospital or going downstairs to a basement; each time a customer entered or left the shop: "What is Cecilia doing now? What's she doing *right now*?"'

Truman fell silent, staring at the section of railing that had been struck by the lightning. Then he pointed his binoculars back up at the stars.

'Did you know that there was a hurricane in America that killed 12,000 people?' Maceo asked. 'It happened on an island called Galveston. The city was flooded and people had to climb onto rooftops to escape the waters. But the buildings collapsed one by one. And in 1970 a cyclone in Bangladesh caused more than a million deaths.'

'Yes, that one I do remember. The Bay of Bengal Cyclone. There was another terrible cyclone after that, about fifteen years ago, which killed about 100,000 people. That's why Man has always looked to the skies, trying to predict what was coming. Great catastrophes can come from the sky: the frosts, the floods, the tornados. Hence all the superstitions and legends – that the world will be destroyed by meteorites or the melting of the polar ice caps; that animals can predict the weather.'

'Is that true?'

'Who knows. They say that if at the start of summer caterpillars have narrower stripes or squirrels bushier tails, it will be a cold winter; that if horses refuse to jump or if ants move in straight lines, it means there'll soon be a storm. Anyway, what does it matter?' said Truman, suddenly. He looked at his watch. 'It's very late already. We both need to get some rest. If you like, we'll continue reading and looking at the sky in the morning.'

The boy started walking to the door but turned just as he was about to leave the room.

'Did I tell you that every day more than 45,000 electric storms hit the Earth?' he said. 'Which means almost 16 million a year.'

'Goodnight. God bless.'

'OK. Good night.'

Truman looked at him affectionately. He wondered how the boy would have looked had he married Cecilia. It was hard to imagine him with different eyes, much darker hair, skin that was more tanned. Right now they wouldn't be here, he thought, but on the other continent, perhaps in Costa Rica, in a yellow-painted house in the Amón district, or in Mexico, in a garden in San Ángel, listening to songs by Augustín Lara, Olga Darson, Elvira Ríos; instead of winter it would be summer; instead of pizza and yogurts for dinner they would have eaten lamb with a bean sauce, and a fruit salad of papaya, soursop, sapodilla plums, and pineapple. It was strange to think how Maceo was both what he most loved and at the same time the tangible proof of everything that he had lost. He felt a great bitterness, he felt the weight of a life of sacrifice and mutilations bearing down on him, a life with so many stories but without a happy ending. What had been the point of all he had done? Nothing – it had all been useless, just things that had happened but that hadn't really mattered.

A second before he fell asleep he remembered how his father used to take him for walks along the banks of the Guadalquivir as a boy, and how they sometimes wrote their names with their fingers on the surface of the water.

'See? It's as if you too were part of the river now.'

III

The small room smelt so strongly of fresh ink that when she breathed in, her lungs seemed to fill with a dark, acidic liquid. For a few moments Ruth stayed where she was, alone and in silence, trying to come to terms with what had just happened to her amid the everyday sounds of office life: the printers, the telephones, the computers, the opening and closing of doors. Then she leant on the photocopier and pressed the button: on paper, duplicated in black and white, the lifelines like cracks, the skin the colour of carbon, her hand appeared that of a corpse. It reminded her of one of those horrible newspaper photographs in which the victims of a fire, plane crash or bomb attack were shown lying in the street, by a burning building, amid the wreckage of a fuselage. She remembered a news item about a man who had just received a hand transplant and how that man was never again going to be able to type or do up the buttons of a shirt, though he would be able to hold a glass or dial a number. Then she returned her thoughts to what had happened when she entered the room with some files and a man called Ignacio had followed her in. She had known him since she first started working there: he was about thirty, from Minorca, the father of a small boy, his wife's name was Lucrecia. What else? Not much, save for the odd detail of the kind which goes towards forming the rather arbitrary image we usually have of our colleagues or fellow students – people with whom we spend much time but share little intimacy, and with whom, in most cases, we have nothing in common except for those hours spent at work. Ignacio was shy, formal, liked cats and sports, smoked in moderation; he was prudent and friendly too, and in her opinion, a conformist, a person resigned to his own fate, and the worst kind of mediocrity: the kind who had no desire to be anything else.

But that morning, on the pretext of looking for some spare paper within the confines of that narrow space, he had, in a more or less overt caress, rested a hand on her hip and invited her for a drink after work, if she wanted to, that is, perhaps they could get to know each other a little better. She had guessed at once – she saw exactly what was happening, what had given rise to this new brazen-not-prudent, bold-not-shy Ignacio; she knew precisely where his forwardness came from, and the reason why he now saw her as a potential conquest, an easy prey: Ramón had told him everything. Who else had he told? Did everyone know? She could hear him saying: 'I fucked her in a hotel, she's got these amazing tits, she sucked me off in the toilet of a bar.' Or maybe it wasn't like that, maybe it was only a coincidence, only her jumping to conclusions?

She did the photocopies and went back to her desk. She tried to concentrate, but could sense the eyes of her colleagues staring at her in silent rebuke. She looked at the photocopy of her hand again. She thought back to the several times in her life when she could have died: the morning her school coach collided with another car, right in the middle of Alameda de Recalde, on the way back to Bilbao from Munguía; or that night during the Easter holidays in Seville, when she'd had a lucky escape – just as she stepped out of the bath an electric hairdryer fell in; or when she'd been so depressed after Maceo was born, and had had severe anaemia.

From these, Ruth's mind jumped to another remarkable story from her past, the one concerning the last years of her father's life: that strange business of which she had become aware only much later, when in order to piece together the figure of a man whom death had shattered into a thousand pieces, as though he'd been a terracotta idol, she had started asking around and discovered that the more pieces she restored the less recognisable he became, and that although the pieces were certainly his, the result was not him. What Ruth had always known was that one day, without warning, her father had gone to bed, never to leave it again. He was not ill nor did he provide a specific reason for his behaviour; he simply locked himself in his room, took to eating one meal a day, and began to spend as much time as possible asleep. Why? That was the question everyone had asked him a thousand times. What's the matter with you? Dad, what's wrong? He would shrug, pull a face, and invariably give the same reply:

'There's nothing I feel like doing.'

When and where had that eccentric behaviour started? What had brought it on? Not only did Ruth never manage to find out, but her astonishment became all the greater on the day of the funeral itself, when, on getting home to Calle Cosme Echebarrieta and sitting down with her mother to look through the family album, she discovered that the deceased had ripped out all photographs of himself. And that wasn't all – in the months prior to his death, as far as Ruth was gradually able to discover, her father had also removed photos of himself belonging to relatives, with the excuse that he wanted to make copies. Which meant that it had not been a sudden fit of rage but a premeditated decision, a meticulously planned extermination. Why? What drove him to want his image erased from the face of the Earth? Against what or whom were his actions directed?

Ruth felt trapped, alone, empty. All around her the office and its employees gave their usual impression of belonging to a vulgar and corrosive world. She remembered her honeymoon in New York yet again, the apartment on Twelfth and Eighth Avenue overlooking the Hudson River, where she and Samuel had stuck little green flags into an atlas, in all the places they were going to visit: Ceylon, Madagascar, the Fiji Islands, Samoa. It had all been a pack of lies, a trap. However had she let herself be taken in like that? Why did she have to pay so dearly for having been tricked? Words of a song by Bob Dylan came to mind: 'Don't commit the crime if you don't want to do the time.' But she didn't agree.

After work she went to a café. She ordered a glass of gin, and then a second. Was she really going to kill Samuel? As always, the answer was no; yet she was still adding a small dose of poison to his food, enough to pay him back for all the harm he had done her. Or maybe it wasn't like that, maybe a little pain was not enough?

She left the café and set off for home. She thought about how unlucky she had been, about the lightning which had struck Maceo on the very evening that she was going to leave Samuel, about how that accident had put everything on hold. Was that really true, though? She was going to leave him to go and live where? To live how? On what? With whom? Or had it all been just another dummy run, another empty threat?

She decided to drop by Marta's apartment. 'Poor Marta's apartment' was how she thought of it. She'd tell her that she was planning to leave Samuel. Perhaps she and Marta could spend some time together, survive in Madrid on their combined salaries, or go and stay with her mother in Bilbao, start again from scratch. Ruth pictured Marta finishing her studies, meeting the man she'd always deserved – a doctor or lawyer, perhaps, someone brilliant and special, someone who was fun, cultured, calm. She also decided to put an end to that whole business with Ramón, to end it for good, to climb out of that hole, walk out of the shadows, step free of the mud. The mere thought of this made her feel better; she felt renewed and happy, like someone finally coming up for air and drawing breath.

She looked up at the sky. Its clarity seemed a good omen, a sign of change, the metaphor for a world that was accessible and propitious once more; proof that the sails were stirring and that the future was on its way.

Did she truly believe in this resurrection, she wondered, or was it merely a game? It made no difference: there and then she didn't care, all she wanted to believe in was that ray of sunshine in the midst of the downpour. She went on her way, feeling a strange sense of energy, the faith of someone attempting to forget a long captivity.

Standing on the other side of the street, in a shop doorway, hidden by passers-by, was Samuel. He watched her get on a bus and went after her in a taxi. Where was she off to? To meet another man? Was there really another man? He slid his hand inside his jacket as though to grip a weapon: a revolver, or perhaps a knife. Alongside Ruth sat a woman reading a novel, and a character in that novel said: 'Evil be to him who carries deserts within.'

When the doorbell rang, Marta was remembering the *nazarenos* she had once seen during the Easter holidays in Seville, the impression the pained stares and cheerless gait of these penitents had made on her at the time, as they filed through the streets dressed in their purple tunics, which were the same colour as one of her cheekbones now.

She ran to the door, intending to throw herself into Lucas's arms and beg his forgiveness, to say she was sorry, it wouldn't happen again, it had all been her fault, please don't go, I'm sorry, I'm sorry, I'm so sorry as she hugged him, I'm sorry as she pulled off his clothes, I'm sorry, I'm sorry, I'm sorry, I'm sorry.

He had hit her harder than ever before, that was true, but it was also true that this time she had been more vicious in her insults, calling him a loser, a son of a bitch, a yob. How had all the shouting and beatings started? When? Why hadn't she run away, instead of staying on in that hell, blinded by her own misfortune, and struggling for something that didn't want to be hers? She remembered the first time he hit her, a couple of weeks before; the shock she had felt at seeing the ferocity of Lucas's eyes, their evil gleam; the sinister sound of the slap, the burning sensation on her skin; and then came the reconciliation, the caresses, the tears. Not long afterwards the same thing happened again, after a night when Lucas had not come home and she had demanded an explanation. And again a couple of days ago, when she had accused him of spending her money: on what, on whom, and where have you been, are you still fucking Luisa, you yob, you son of a bitch, you loser. She had not seen him since. She handed in her notice at work and stayed at home, waiting for him, all of Thursday, all of Friday, the entire weekend, as afraid that he would return as that he wouldn't; she installed a bolt on the door, then put flowers in the bedroom; she went to a police station, which she couldn't face entering, then went back and cooked several of his favourite dishes; she bought make-up to hide her bruises and tone down the yellow-and-purple swelling on her cheek where Lucas had punched her.

Which is why, on opening the door, only to find her mother standing there, her smile faded, her defences collapsed; she felt a terrifying sense of despondency, a total eclipse. Then, on seeing the surprise and the alarm in Ruth's eyes, Marta remembered her own wounds, and all at once, she felt all the shame, all the humiliation, all the fear. Finally these feelings gave way to a kind of hesitant, melancholy joy, the joy of someone who, returning home from exile after a war, after surviving atrocities and abuses, enduring cold and hunger, after putting up with insults and epidemics, sleeping outdoors in the rain, in the snow, after being hunted by dogs and machine-gunned pitilessly by enemy planes, sees the borders of their homeland at last, catches sight once more of a world without whips or crimes or torture, a world which they no longer believed existed, which they thought was already gone for ever.

Ruth, for her part, was unable to utter a word; she brought a hand up to her mouth, as if to muffle a scream or stop herself vomiting; then she reached out with her other hand to touch Marta's face, running a finger over the purple cheekbone, the swollen eyelid, and drew her daughter into her arms. Her body felt frail and gave off a sweet smell; they were both trembling violently, as if by touch, each one's anguish and suffering had spread to each other.

'Oh, my God!' Ruth said. 'My little darling.'

'I . . . I loved him so much . . . I . . . I'm so sorry . . .'

Ruth placed a finger over her lips: *ssshhh*, there's no need to talk. That was when Lucas turned up, along with the two others. What happened next? Years later, each would have their own version: Ruth hurled herself at him, calling him a miserable bastard, a coward; Lucas had come back to ask Marta for money, yet again; the two others were petty criminals, and, some time later, Ruth would be sure she recognised the face of one of them alongside a newspaper article about a drugs shipment and a settling of scores. No doubt Lucas owed them money; or maybe he, too, was a criminal; or was it her imagining all this, and the truth was they were just two friends who had come to help him to collect his belongings.

What else?

There was definitely shouting and a struggle; the two young thugs held Ruth back so that Lucas could hit Marta. Someone turned the radio full up; someone ripped Ruth's shirt, perhaps by accident, perhaps not. What would have happened next? What was the blare of the radio intended to drown out? They would never know, for at that moment Samuel stormed onto the scene; he shoved the person holding Ruth to the ground, grabbed Lucas's arm before he had another chance to hit his daughter. What was Samuel doing there? Could it have been a coincidence? He would always maintain that it was, that he had suddenly decided to visit Marta on impulse. Ruth found so much coincidence suspicious; she would think many things about that particular morning, including the truth: Samuel had been following her. What for? Since when? Did he know about Ramón? Samuel threw himself at one of the men, got kicked, then punched. He fell down, picked himself up, they knocked him down again.

The way he talked about it afterwards, the other three all got their share of the punches – in the eye, nose, liver, jab-jab, left hook, left cross, right hook, uppercut. In fact, what Samuel actually did during the fight was to play a role, feign a skill that was not his, just as he had done at university when he met Ruth, when at meetings he used to repeat other people's words – phrases he found in Truman's books and patiently underlined when he was alone, storing them up for the right moment, the perfect opportunity, lying in wait to plunge them like knives into the heart of conversations: 'If we only put up walls, we'll be left isolated; but if into those walls we put windows, on the inside we'll have light and on the outside, storms'; 'To legalise is easier than to legitimise'; 'No truth that hides other truths can be the truth' . . . He struck out wildly with two punches, someone head-butted him and broke his nose, Ruth rushed out onto the landing and screamed for help.

I fought well, he told himself afterwards, when that absurd fight was over. He felt at peace, he felt that this time he had not let anyone down; he was bleeding from various wounds, and to him this seemed a hero's blood; Ruth and Marta were with him, the three of them there together, safe, alone. He felt content. 'Nothing will be the same again,' he told himself, 'from now on everything will get better, everything will get back to how it was before.' Already he was a different man, a new Samuel; he could almost see it happening before his very eyes, this new man breaking away from his predecessor and hurrying off, leaving him behind for ever.

CHAPTER SIX

What exactly had those years brought them? For what had they struggled? What had they won or lost in that struggle? It was hard to tell, hard to find reasons for all the pain, anguish, and hatred – things that were immense on the inside and invisible on the outside, so patent yet so insubstantial too. Ruth stared up at the clear, menacing sky above the cemetery. What had she learnt on her journey to the edge, her journey beyond herself? That you can share dreams, but not broken dreams. What else? Very little. Nothing almost, except for the rules of destruction, the road to scars. Looking back she saw ruins of what had never been a palace, wounded who had never taken part in a battle. Perhaps her mistake had been to try and give each and every act or event a meaning; or to have had hopes, ambitions. What was the point? Hopes were simply the uppermost part of failure, they were what made failure seem so hurtful, so undeserved. Hopes prevented people from being good. She breathed in the dense fragrance of the flowers; it made her feel sick, it felt like something cold and solid, and seemed to move chaotically, almost liquidly about inside her, like a small red reptile across a wall. She gave Maceo's hand a squeeze as the coffin began its descent into the grave.

Marta, too, noticed something unpleasant about that heavy perfume, which reminded her of the taste of blood. She wondered what had become of Lucas, if he was missing her as well. She had left the job at the clinic and had not been back to the secretarial college; she had spent a few weeks living with Iraide, because she couldn't bear the thought, she told her, of returning to her own apartment: 'What's the point, I don't want to be there if he's not going to phone.' Then she had gone back to live with her parents, back to attending morning lectures at the university. But there was no denying that she felt different now, as if all that had happened meant she no longer fitted back into her old surroundings. It had made her incompatible with those around her, as if it had placed something inside her that others knew nothing of, something that could never be shared, something that set her apart from all else: from a girl called Eneko, who had just moved and now lived in Calle Islas Filipinas – her room had a balcony, during the move there'd been a storm, and she and her two sisters got soaked; from a student called Antonio, who didn't believe the story about the American mountaineers who swore that on Everest, at 8,300 metres, they'd found the body of George Mallory, the first climber ever to have reached the summit – 'Look, it's bound to be a hoax, they're saying they found his name sewn into his clothes and that they buried him back in the snow'; from the lecturer who taught them about the properties of the skin and wrote a list up on the blackboard – Meissner corpuscles give us our sense of touch, Krause and Rufini corpuscles enable us to feel heat and cold.

Where would Lucas be now? Was he thinking of her? She certainly remembered their moments of happiness together, that barely glimpsed paradise which had left her feeling like the person who returns ashore just as the boat is about to weigh anchor, after saying goodbye to relatives, after experiencing for a few moments that feeling of imminent departure, the smell of the cabins, the faint motion of the waves felt through the deck. Lucas, his eyes, his hands – that thorn which Samuel had told her about, the thorn that sticks in a finger and passes all the way up the veins to the heart. Where did you find the strength to keep on struggling for the so many things that didn't matter to you when you had already lost the one thing that did? Did time really bring balance? Would it really soothe and heal? 'Life goes on,' Ruth had told her, and Marta thought about what that meant: someone gets off a train, someone walks a dog, a man pushes his lawnmower, the woman who owned the butcher's switches on the radio. What did any of that have to do with her? Javier Marías had a new book out; jungles in Asia were being cut down so teak from the forests of Cambodia and Indonesia could be used to make garden furniture; Irving Mallory was a friend of Virginia Woolf's, he took a photograph of himself standing naked on a glacier in Tibet, at the foot of Everest, he could recite all of *King Lear* by heart.

Did Lucas have any regrets? Did he want to start again from scratch? The sensation of pain was produced by thousands of nerve endings, of which the human body had as many as two hundred per square centimetre. Iraide had seen him one night in a bar, in the distance, laughing. Laughing about what? With whom? Others had told her that he was now going out with Enara. Marta looked around her. She felt incapable of crying, but it did all seem so awful – the cypresses, the family vaults, the crosses, Ruth and Maceo holding hands, the funeral music coming from somewhere or other, the sound the earth made as it landed on the lid of the coffin, that sound which grew fainter and fainter, less and less distinct, like the slowing heartbeat of a dying man.

Maceo stood staring at the grave, watching the men apply the cement, throw in the pulley ropes, lay the tombstone in place, which made a spine-chilling sound, a sound that meant *for ever, never again*; and as if the one were the logical or natural consequence of the other, he remembered what Truman had told him about Samuel's birth:

'It was 1955. I had been back in Spain for seven years. The year before, two things happened – I married Aitana and my father died. My life had something . . . what's the word . . . something servile about it, do you know what I mean? It's hard to explain; I was living with your grandmother, I was about to become a father, business was so good we could afford to hire an assistant, and there were days when I stayed at home until mid-morning, reading. I bought myself new editions of Ovid, Virgil, and Homer, and one or two volumes by writers who were in exile, such as Luis Cernuda or León Felipe, though most of their works were banned. It was a way, I suppose, of preserving a bit of the past, maintaining a link. Do you understand?'

'Yes,' Maceo said, 'I think I do. But I'm not sure.'

'My father told me a story about the day they came to kill him. He was in that lorry, along with three or four other prisoners; he didn't know where they were being taken, though he certainly knew why, especially when they got to the meadow and he saw the bodies of the men who'd been shot up against the wall of the football ground – half a dozen corpses, lying there with that horrific look bodies have when they have met with a violent death: the absurd postures, the ransacked faces.'

'Was he afraid?'

'Yes, of course he was. He was frightened, very frightened. Just as he was being taken off the lorry, the car with the Falangists that Delia had called arrived, and they managed to save his life. That's the main part of what happened. But there was something else, a small detail that always made a big impression on me: in the midst of all the confusion, with the murderers and the Falangists all shouting at one another, trying to assert their own authority, my father stooped to pick a bullet off the ground. A bullet that must have fallen out of some rifle. And he kept it, perhaps as proof that it had all really happened. I can still remember the way he would look at it, time and again, towards the end of his life, whenever he talked about the hardships he suffered during the war: about their cold, damp, miserable attic in La Coruña; about the nights in Santa Comba or Vila de Cruces when he stole tungsten for the Germans, on the banks of the Deza. All of a sudden he'd take that bullet out and stare at it, not saying a word, as if condensed inside were all the drama, all the pain, all the sadness. When it comes down to it, life is ethereal but objects are solid, which is why . . .' Truman seemed tired, reluctant to say more.

'What happened when my father was born?'

'One of those incredible twists of fate. While Aitana was in the operating theatre I went out to buy her some roses; just as I entered the florists I met Juan Garcés. Remember him? That man from Las Palmas I met in Costa Rica, the son of the owner of the Solera pharmacy in the Central Market.'

'Yes, I remember Juan Garcés. You were with him at the dance on Puntarenas Beach, in the Hotel Tioga, the first time you saw Cecilia.'

'Exactly. So I asked him about her. How was she? Had she got married? He stopped me before I could say another word. He told me that she had leukaemia, cancer of the blood; she had only a few months left to live. We didn't talk much after that. It was awful the way reality suddenly invaded my memories, a shocking reality that distorted and undermined everything I remembered, filling it with pain and needles and hospitals. By the time I got back to the clinic Samuel was already born. I picked him up in my arms, but all I could think about was Cecilia and her illness. The word 'cancer' comes from the word 'crab'; it got the name from the way it seems to crawl through its victims, devouring them slowly; cutting off, colonising, eating away at every nook and cranny. It was an awful thing to think about as I held my son in my arms. I think . . . well, I think that in that instant something broke, snapped for ever. Your father and I have never been as close as we should have.'

Maceo heard these words again, superimposed now over the sound of the gravediggers, sealing in place the tombstone on which was chiselled the name of the person who had pronounced them shortly before dying. Maceo decided that he would go to live in Central America before too long, perhaps in Costa Rica or Mexico; and that in San José he would embark on a search for Cecilia's descendants. He pictured a sweet and beautiful young woman with jet-black hair, isosceles legs, and brown eyes with a drop of gorse yellow at their centre. In that instant, in Madrid, Ruth gave his hand a squeeze. Ten or twelve years later, in El Salvador, Maceo went down into the crater of the Quezaltepec, where for that young woman, he cut an orchid from among the many growing inside the volcano.

Samuel stood on the other side of the grave, facing his family. He thought of the happy days that had come a few months earlier, in the wake of the fight in Marta's apartment. He remembered how, that same evening, Ruth and he had made love, for the first time in so long; and how the next morning, he had gone to an estate agency to put their apartment up for sale and then to a travel agency to ask about prices, routes, best times of the year to go travelling. He had given Ruth the choice of Brazil or Samoa – Ipanema beach or Stevenson's tomb, Copacabana or the island where the natives gave you their names. He had been to the university too, to enquire about exams, lectureships, the likelihood of obtaining a good post, something a little more worthy of the two of them than the steelworks. About the money he had in a secret account, he said nothing to his wife. But what difference could it make?

Matters, however, had gradually cooled: the apartment was proving hard to sell, the idea of living above a butcher's held little appeal, likewise the different-sized rooms and open balconies. The exams for a lectureship required a lot of free time, which he didn't have. As for Brazil and Samoa, it was all so expensive . . . They needed to go, but all in good time. Ruth again seemed disappointed.

He looked back at the tombstone, at the names of his parents, one next to the other, Aitana and Truman, together for all eternity, beyond the grave. He hardly remembered his mother, the sweet Aitana: always so silent, so out of place, in her overalls, her pale nail varnish, chatting to customers in the grocery. What else? Very little: her soft, somewhat devious voice, her slightly rough hands, that measured way she had of speaking to Truman. And her death, so many years ago now; that sudden surge of death, that world of sanatoria, flowers, surgeons.

They left the cemetery. All around Maceo everything seemed strange, inexplicable. He slipped a hand into his pocket and felt the keys he'd found in Samuel's duffel coat. Why he liked them so much, he could not have said, yet he felt drawn to them as though they hid a mystery, a clue to something that had once secretly taken place. He would go to Central America to look for what Truman had left behind; but perhaps taking a longer, more circuitous route, via Beijing, New Delhi, Tokyo. What would happen, he wondered, if he took out a map and marked in blue all the journeys Truman had made? What shape would emerge if he linked the points of each trip with the next? In a way, these lines would make up a constellation just like those in the sky – the Truman galaxy, complete with its own gods and heroes.

In China, Maceo worked as a news correspondent and stayed in a run-down guest house where, by the light of an oil lamp and with only a fan to ward off the stifling heat, he read the books Truman had told him about. In Japan, one night, he was set upon by four assassins in a warehouse down by the quayside. After fighting them off, for some reason he remembered the comet and the night he and Truman had watched its progress across the sky through their binoculars.

Ruth, too, recalled that night, which was when she had started poisoning Samuel. The days of calm that followed the fight in Marta's apartment had been so strange; it had been so strange to make love with him again, to be taken in again by the same old lies: Samoa, a new home, a better future, a different Samuel. She had almost begun to love him once more – which was why she now hated him twice as much. She felt so alone and despicable, so humiliated to see herself going back to his bed without the slightest scruple, like a dog trotting over to a scaffold to lap up a victim's blood.

Now, as they walked away from Truman's grave, Samuel took her hand in his, but she shrugged him off. He didn't mind – it was only a passing phase. Things would sort themselves out, he was sure. In recent days, after a respite of two weeks, he'd once more had to start feigning the dizziness, coughing, and retching, when he realised that Ruth had started poisoning him again. In fact he had known about this ever since the afternoon he killed the cat by the abandoned house, ever since the moment he decided to spy on Ruth, watch her every move, follow her every step. From then on, every time she added the murderous powder to his food, it was no longer rat poison, just plain flour – flour mixed with a few drops of Coca-Cola. Every night, before he went to bed, Samuel would carefully weigh the box of poison; if the weight had dropped by a few grams, he would put on his act: laboured breathing, moans, shivering. 'Poor Ruth,' he thought, 'she's so ingenuous, so easy to catch out!'

He wondered if he would ever be able to confess the truth to her, one day when they were out of danger – 'out of the red zone', as he liked to put it, taking the expression from the section on dials that tells you when you're at risk: when the temperature is too high, the speed too great, the fuel too low. Three or four years would have passed; they'd be sitting in a restaurant, the kind of place that served exotic local food in an ambience of accordion music and oil lamps; in Paris or Venice maybe, by the river or alongside one of the canals; and she would have asked him if he still loved her. And he, at last, would say to her the words of a poem, which, so far in advance, he had

already picked out and marked in pencil in a book by
Pablo Neruda:

> *Not only fire burns between us,*
> *But all a life,*
> *the simple story,*
> *the simple love*
> *of a woman and a man*
> *like everyone else.*

That was exactly the way it would happen. That was all
he was going to say. Not a word more.

This novel is dedicated to Ángeles Prado, who never opened a wound or poisoned a word; who always gives her everything without asking for anything in return. Others have a piece of my heart, but she has it all.